INTERACTIVE COMPUTING WITH
BASIC
A FIRST COURSE

DONALD M. MONRO

Lecturer in Electrical Engineering,
Imperial College of Science and Technology

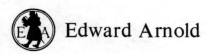
Edward Arnold

First published 1974
by Edward Arnold (Publishers) Ltd
25 Hill Street, London WIX 8LL

ISBN: 0 7131 2488 1

For Andrew

Printed in Great Britain by William Clowes & Sons Limited,
London, Colchester and Beccles

PREFACE

This book has arisen through the need for a structured text on BASIC for first year students in Electrical Engineering at Imperial College. These students use the College time sharing facilities to bring themselves to a common level of expertise in problem solving by computer through this series of practical sessions. The course is also suitable for schools and, with the introduction of computing into the schools curriculum, it is possible that at some future time the majority of our new students already will have mastered the equivalent of the first eight sessions presented here or their equivalent, so making this course unnecessary at university level.

The choice of BASIC (Beginners All-purpose Symbolic Instruction Code) for this purpose is not unusual because its syntax is amenable enough that the computing science becomes the primary concern, as it should. The emphasis here is on the numerical and practical aspects of computing, and efficient programming style is stressed throughout. I have tried to introduce the BASIC language gradually and in a logical order; for example, I do not believe the READ, DATA and RESTORE statements to be self-evident and these are not introduced until session 8, when their usefulness is at least obvious.

Some assumptions must be made about the mathematical background to any course. This one could coincide with the first exposure to calculus, or ideally come a bit later. Sessions 1–8 by themselves form a complete course in elementary BASIC and some useful applications. Session 9 adds the matrix facilities for those with the necessary background. These sessions should describe a subset of BASIC which conforms to common practice. The remaining sessions 10 and 11 do not follow in logical sequence but are included for completeness. It is impossible to describe any existing BASIC system as standard because its development has been uneven; however a Specification for Standard BASIC* has been published recently which should have a beneficial effect. This course is a subset of that specification. The most significant omissions are the file manipulation statements and the additional library functions which may exist.

Our present course is organized around a single lecture introducing the particular time-sharing system and a series of practical sessions during which the students follow the text but omit the supplementary problems. The level of the course could be adjusted to less advanced students through more formal instruction or to more advanced students by using the supplementary problems which are of a higher mathematical level. It is recommended that instructors basing a course on this text should prepare a separate description of the logging in and out procedures and a list of useful system commands.

I should like to acknowledge the active encouragement of Professor B. McA. Sayers of the Engineering in Medicine Laboratory at Imperial College for my first chance to try BASIC on an Experimental Course in Scientific Methods for medical doctors, organized by Dr. S. P. Vahl and

---

* Bull, G. M., Freeman, W. and Garland, S. J., *Specification for Standard BASIC*, NCC Publications, The National Computing Centre, Manchester (1973).

supported by the Leverhulme Foundation. In the Electrical Engineering Department I am grateful to Mr. J. M. Howl for his support throughout the development of this course, and to Professor John Brown and Dr. D. Jones for making it possible. I was also fortunate in the help of Mr. J. L. Branch and Mr. R. G. Becker in seeing the preliminary version through its first year and making many valuable suggestions for its improvement. A platoon of typists has worked on this at one time or another and I am grateful to them all: Sarah Green, Alison Elliott, Joan Tomlinson, Nina Hay, and Rita McBride.

1974   D. M. Monro
                                                           Imperial College, London.

CONTENTS

INTRODUCTION

1 Why BASIC

This book is intended for people who are fortunate enough to have access to a computer system with interactive BASIC and who wish to solve mathematical problems using computers. Why then should BASIC be the first approach? The answer lies in the simplicity of BASIC, which was first developed as a language for beginners and expresses instructions for the computer in an easily understood form. All languages have rules of grammar, and for computing the rules must be very precise so that the instructions given to the computer are exact. The student will probably be interested in one of the traditional 'big' languages but these abound with complicated sets of rules for different situations. If one of these languages is tackled by a novice, many rules have to be learned before the simplest program can be tried and more initial effort is expended on the language than on the computing. However the grammar of BASIC is intentionally simplified so that the student learns a few simple rules and immediately can produce results. At the same time BASIC has all the essential facilities for computation. Therefore the emphasis can be placed on the style and methods of computer programming. Furthermore the student has not wasted his time because of the strong resemblance between BASIC and the 'big' languages to which he can easily convert when his knowledge of computing is good enough. This course is designed to take a person to that level, from which a transition to such a language as FORTRAN, ALGOL, COBOL, or PL/I can be made.

2 Computers as Stupid Slaves

Computing machinery is just another tool that man has invented to strengthen his powers, in this case for the repetitive numerical manipulations which his earlier inventions have necessitated. A computer has no personality of its own; anything it does is the result of human instruction. Every computer is built with a repertoire of simple orders which it slavishly obeys. The machine has no way of knowing if the instructions given to it are what the programmer really intended. It interprets them literally and could quite easily get stuck repeating the same meaningless operation, until human intervention or a timing circuit intervened. The computer that accidentally issues electricity bills is following human instruction, however mistaken. By any definition of intelligence computing machinery rates as zero.

However in its stupidity it is extremely fast. Provided it is instructed properly it can outdistance in seconds or minutes a human lifetime of hand calculation. This is the reason for the profound effect computers have already had on society. Computers can add a million numbers a second, and most can multiply nearly as rapidly. A computer can store thousands or tens of thousands of results in its 'memory' and recall any one of them in a microsecond. It can be programmed to make decisions by examining these results and so can be given a superficial appearance of intelligence—but it is intelligence transferred from the programmer and the computer's mistakes are nearly always the programmer's mistakes.

3 Computer Systems

A computer system is much more than a machine which does calculations. For the machine to be useful it must be surrounded by devices which feed it information and it must be filled with programs to guide it through its various tasks. The person using interactive BASIC will communicate through a terminal having a keyboard for him to transmit information to the BASIC system and a printer for the responses of BASIC. The most common keyboard arrangement is shown in Fig. 1.

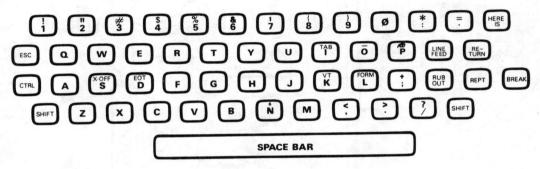

Fig. 1

The letters are in the familiar typewriter positions but there are many other facilities which may be unfamiliar. The user of BASIC will have to know where to find most of these keys, noting particularly the 'carriage return' and 'control' keys.

A computer also could have connected to it readers and punches for cards and paper tape, magnetic tape transports, line printers and magnetic disk storage. All these devices provide 'input' (to the computer) and 'output' (from the computer) of information. Each device will require a 'driver' program to control it and there will be a program to supervise the drivers (and probably a program to monitor the supervisor). All these devices and programs make up the computer system before BASIC arrives on the scene and before the computer 'user' arrives to try his program, as in Fig. 2.

The computer itself is not likely to understand BASIC—the language obeyed by computers is a rather nasty series of numbers. Therefore a translation program is needed which takes a BASIC program and converts it to the 'machine language'. The program which does this is called a 'compiler' or an 'interpreter' depending on the details of its operation. Thus the computer system that waits for the BASIC programmer is an imposing collection of machinery ('hardware') and programs ('software'). It is fortunate for the beginner that the design of BASIC protects him from the need for detailed knowledge of all this.

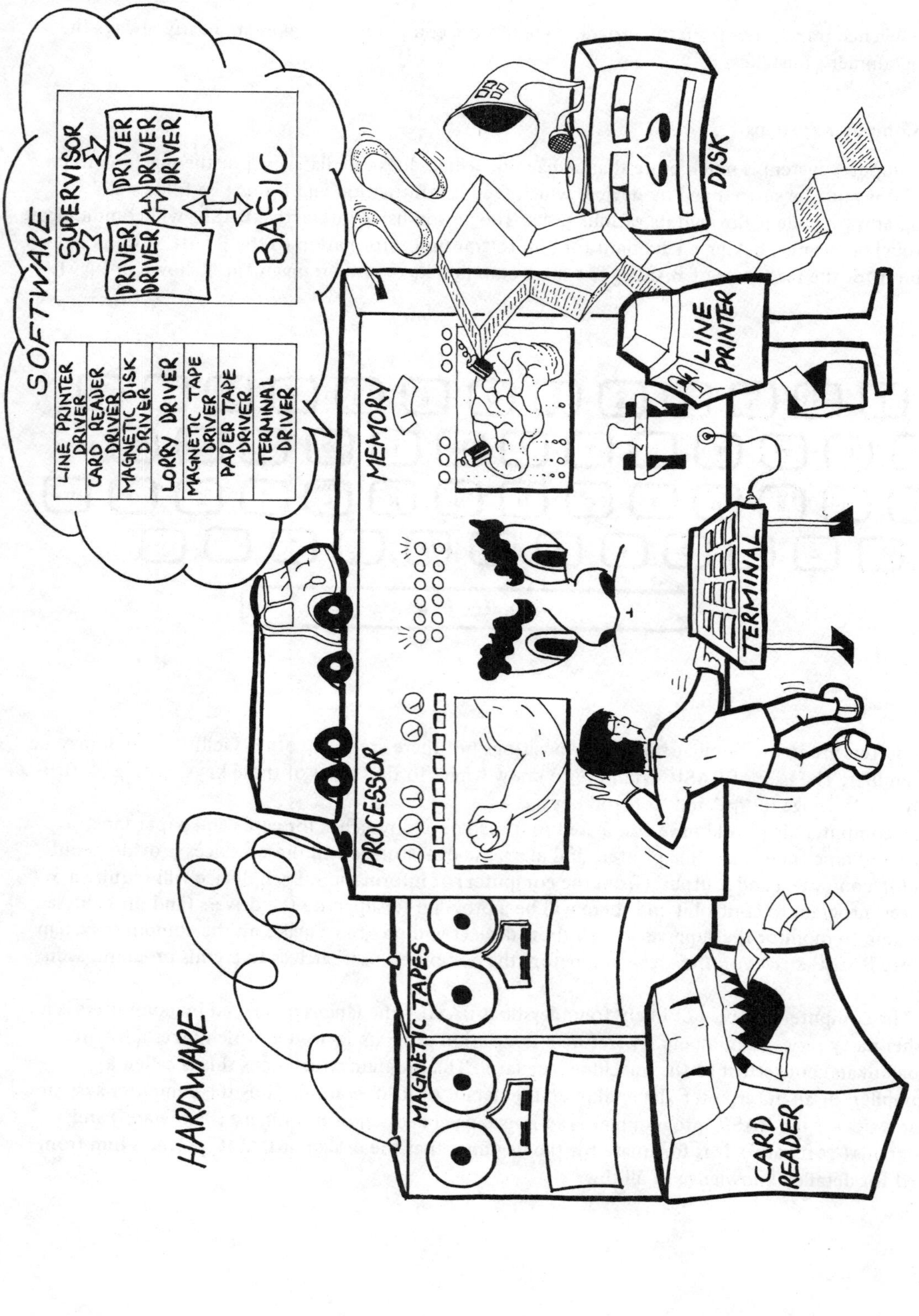
SOFTWARE
LINE PRINTER DRIVER
CARD READER DRIVER
MAGNETIC DISK DRIVER
LORRY DRIVER
MAGNETIC TAPE DRIVER
PAPER TAPE DRIVER
TERMINAL DRIVER
SUPERVISOR
DRIVER
DRIVER
DRIVER
DRIVER
DRIVER
BASIC
HARDWARE
MAGNETIC TAPES
PROCESSOR
MEMORY
DISK
LINE PRINTER
TERMINAL
CARD READER

Fig. 2

4 Interactive Computing and Time Sharing

Early computer systems were organized to deal with one program at a time, and programs were normally presented to the system in groups or 'batches' which the machine processed one after the other. The programmer submitted his program to a computing service which ran it for him and returned the result some time later. BASIC like any other language can be run in this way, and the majority of computing is still done in batches. The disadvantage of batch processing for small programs and for learning is that the 'turnaround' time is unlikely to be less than a few hours and is more likely to be measured in days.

An interactive computer system puts the programmer into direct communication with the computer, usually through a typewriter terminal. Therefore the turnaround time for developing programs and finding and correcting errors in them is reduced to seconds. The program itself can be written so that the programmer gives it information while the computer is executing it and so he can control the steps of the calculation as it progresses. When BASIC is run in an interactive system, programs can be developed rapidly and tested and corrected from a terminal. The learning process is both shortened and made more thorough because the rapid response of the computer and the straightforward nature of the language work in the student's favour and encourage experimentation.

An interactive computer system can be in one of two modes of operation as seen by the programmer. These modes are 'program definition' and 'program execution' and are distinguished by whether the programmer or the computer is in control of events as in Fig. 3. In the program definition mode the programmer will be creating, editing and correcting his program and is himself in control. The main flow of information is from the terminal to the computer and any response by the computer is a result of the programmer's activities. As will be seen in Session 1, he can enter commands to the system, and the effect of some of these commands is to transfer control to the computer. If this is done, the system will change to execution mode and the user will be required to respond only if the program has made specific provision for input from the terminal. The main flow of information will be from the computer to the terminal, and the programmer normally will regain control when the program is finished, although he can stop execution manually if necessary.

Time sharing is a means of making the resources of one computer system serve the needs of many users at the same time. The computer does not do several things at once, but it can be made to jump from one task to another so rapidly that the individual user is not aware of any long delays. Therefore interactive computing can be carried out at many terminals 'simultaneously'. Large time sharing systems can service a hundred or more terminals all using a variety of languages to perform different operations, and also can do batch and other work at the same time. Small time sharing systems also exist, and some which are dedicated to BASIC only can service 16 or more terminals with a computer less expensive than the group of terminals. The BASIC language may be run by batch or interactive means, and if it is interactive it could be either dedicated to one terminal or time shared by several.

5 How to Use this Book

First of all, it is necessary to have a means of running BASIC programs on a computer, ideally by access to an interactive system. If only batch processing is available the course can still be followed but some obvious omissions will have to be made. If possible a source of expert advice should be

Programmer in control

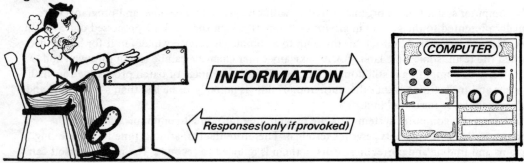

Definition Mode - the programmer is entering, editing or correcting his program

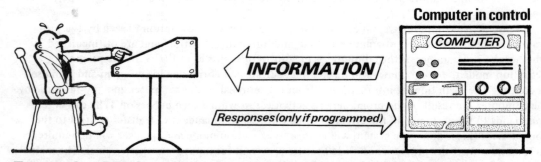

Computer in control

Execution Mode - the computer is executing a program

Fig. 3

available, not so much about BASIC as about the computer system and the terminal. The first job is to learn how to log in and out of BASIC and then the Sessions can be tackled in order. All the exercises should be done because they provide exploration and clarification of details which are vital to the learning process. As far as possible all the problems within each Session should be attempted. The supplementary problems at the end of most Sessions are more demanding and should be regarded as optional.

Each Session should be read through before it is tried, and even the most tentative outline of the solution to a problem will save time spent at the terminal. Nothing is more futile than reading the material for the first time and trying to think out the solutions at the keyboard. Each session should take between two and three hours at a terminal—if it takes less, so much the better, but if it requires more then either preparation is inadequate or the level of the course is inappropriate for the particular student's background and interests.

SESSION 1
ARITHMETIC IN BASIC

1 Introduction

One of the advantages of BASIC as a first computing language is that a relatively small amount of information is required to apply it in a useful way. Like any computing language, BASIC has rules of construction, or grammar, which define what can be done, and how the language is to be interpreted by the computer. This session first introduces the simplest kind of BASIC program and then proceeds to elaborate on the rules of arithmetic as they apply to BASIC. By the end of this session it is possible to use BASIC as a programmable calculator for the evaluation of complicated expressions. Because of the amount of detail conveyed in this session, the all important ability of a program to control its own destiny is left to the next session. It is assumed here that the student knows (or can find out) how to activate his terminal for the use of BASIC.

2 A Simple Program in BASIC—the PRINT and END statements

A computer program in BASIC is an ordered series of instructions to the computer, written as statements using familar English and mathematical terms. Such a program has an explicit meaning which is clear to the programmer and precise for computer interpretation.

The following is an example of a very simple BASIC program of two lines, each of which makes a statement of the programmer's intentions:

```
10 PRINT 5/7
20 END
```

The program instructs the computer first to evaluate the arithmetic expression 5/7 (5 divided by 7) and then to print the result. Two important features of BASIC are evident in this example

(i) Each of the two lines begins with a line number. These line numbers dictate the order of events when a BASIC program is obeyed, as in the flow diagram. Every line must therefore begin with a line number.

(ii) The program ends with an END statement. Every BASIC program must have an END statement as its highest numbered line.

Two different statements of BASIC appear in this simple program, the PRINT statement, and the END statement. The intention of this program should be clear; in line 10 a quotient (5/7) is to be evaluated and printed, and the program ends at line 20.

The meaning of programs often can be clarified by the use of a flow chart, which shows diagrammatically the steps involved in a computer program and their order. The flow chart, Fig. 1.1, represents this simple program.

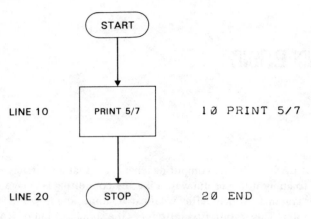

Fig. 1.1. Flow chart for a very simple BASIC program.

Before the program can be used, it must be entered into the computer, and then it must be possible to edit it to correct errors. It is also important to be able to examine the program held by the computer by 'listing' it line by line on the terminal. Finally, the program can be 'run', when the computer will obey the instructions given in the program, in this case by evaluating the quotient 5/7 and printing the result. The next sections show how programs can be created, edited, listed, and run.

3 Creating BASIC Programs

Newcomers to interactive computing will find difficulty in distinguishing the various facilities which are simultaneously available at the terminal. A common confusion arises in separating the response of the computer system when programs are being created from the quite different behaviour of the terminal when a program is being run. While creating a program it is possible to enter lines of the program, to edit the program by adding, changing or deleting lines, and to call upon certain other facilities of the computer system.

Entering and editing operations simply consist of typing in the desired lines of BASIC each beginning with a line number. Any line of information which begins with a numeric character (∅-9) will therefore be treated as a line of BASIC. Any line beginning with a letter or other symbol, on the other hand, will be treated as a command to the computer system. Thus when a program is not being run the rule is very straightforward: lines of program begin with a number whereas lines beginning with anything else are treated as commands to the system. The usefulness of commands and the behaviour while running a program will be introduced later in this session.

The sample program can be entered by typing it. Each separate line is entered and terminated with the 'carriage return' key. The order in which the lines are entered is unimportant because the correct sequence is given explicitly by the line numbers. It is usual for the line numbers not to be consecutive, since the programmer may later wish to insert extra lines between those of the original program. In the example the line numbers are separated by 10, although an increment of 100 is often used.

EXERCISE   Enter the sample program:

```
10 PRINT 5/7
20 END
```

Do not attempt to correct errors at this stage.

4 Listing BASIC Programs—the command LIST

Typing mistakes can easily occur in entering a BASIC program, and errors in transmission between the terminal and computer are possible. Therefore, once a BASIC program has been entered, it is crucial to be able to examine it as it is known to the computer system. The system command LIST is provided for this purpose, and causes the current version of the program to be printed on the terminal.

EXERCISE   Type in the command LIST to obtain a listing of the sample program.

5 Editing BASIC Programs

It is very likely that typing or other mistakes will be made when a program is entered, so that the means of editing programs must be provided. With BASIC it is possible to change lines, insert new lines, and eliminate unwanted ones. Because each line of BASIC has a line number, the procedure is very simple: when a new line is typed in, it becomes part of the program. Thus the procedures are:

(i) To replace or correct a line: type in the new line in full, and 'carriage return'.

Example   The program reads

```
10 PRANT 5/7
20 END
```

You type in

```
10 PRINT 5/7
```
and 'carriage return'

The program then reads

```
10 PRINT 5/7
20 END
```

(ii) To insert a line: type in the new line with a suitable line number, and 'carriage return'. For example a new line numbered 15 could be inserted between lines 10 and 20 of the sample program.

Example   The program reads

```
10 PRINT 5/7
20 END
```

You type in

```
15 PRINT 7/5
```

The program then reads

```
10 PRINT 5/7
15 PRINT 7/5
20 END
```

(iii) To eliminate a line: type in only the line number, and 'carriage return'.

Example   The program reads

```
10 PRINT 5/7
15 PRINT 7/5
20 END
```

You type in

```
15                      (just the line number and 'carriage return' with no blank spaces)
```

The program then reads

```
10 PRINT 5/7
20 END
```

Note that to correct a line, the new version has to be typed in full. This is sometimes tedious so that careful typing is always worthwhile. Most systems also provide a means of correcting characters in a line while it is being typed. On the keyboard there will be a character which eliminates the previous character entered. Usually this is a ←('back arrow') but on some keyboards it may be an __('underline'). Thus an incorrect symbol in a line of program (or a command) can be removed by typing in sufficient 'back arrows' or 'underlines' to remove the error, and typing of the line can be continued from the corrected symbol. For example the line

```
10 PRA←INP 5/7←←←←←T 5/7
```

is the same as

```
1 Ø  PRINT  5/7
```

The blank between T and 5 counts as a character.

> EXERCISE   Experiment with the editing facilities to add, change, and delete lines in the sample program. Try correcting errors when typing a line using 'back arrows'. Finally, restore the program to its given form and list it to be sure.

6 Running BASIC Programs—the command RUN

So far in this session the sample program has been established, edited, and listed, but it has not been tried. The system command RUN is provided to initiate the running of a program. After RUN has been entered, the computer begins to execute the instructions given by the program. While the program is running the behaviour of the terminal is controlled by the program, and it is not possible to edit the program or use other commands until it is finished. The sample program will terminate itself at the END statement.

> EXERCISE   Run the sample program, by typing in RUN

> EXERCISE   Try other expressions by changing line 10, using the operations

+ addition	(example	`1 Ø  PRINT  5+7`)
− subtraction	(example	`1 Ø  PRINT  5-7`)
* multiplication	(example	`1 Ø  PRINT  5*7`)
/ division	(example	`1 Ø  PRINT  5/7`)
↑ exponentiation	(example	`1 Ø  PRINT  5↑7`)

Brackets (parentheses) can be used provided every '(' is matched by a ')'
If a combination of operators is used, the result may be unexpected, for example in

```
1 Ø  PRINT  3/4*5
```

7 Rules of Arithmetic in BASIC

Arithmetic expressions can be written whose intention is clear to the person writing them, but whose meaning is actually ambiguous. The use of brackets (parentheses) clarifies the meaning of such expressions, and any number of these can be used in pairs so that every '(' is matched by a ')'.
For example the statement

```
1 Ø  PRINT  4+5/7
```

could be clarified by the addition of brackets to mean either

$$4+(5/7) \qquad \text{add } 5/7 \text{ to } 4$$
$$\text{or} \quad (4+5)/7 \qquad \text{divide } 4+5 \text{ by } 7$$

The actual meaning of 4+5/7 to BASIC is defined by a set of rules which apply to arithmetic expressions in BASIC. A clear understanding of the rules is essential to any programmer, since mistakes in the interpretation of arithmetic expressions are a very common and often subtle source of programming error.

In BASIC, the rules of arithmetic are expressed in terms of a hierarchy of operations in which operations of high priority are performed before those of low priority. The order of hierarchy is:

( )	quantities in brackets	high
↑	exponentiation	
*/	multiplication and division	
+ −	addition and subtraction	low

Hence in the expression 4+5/7, division has a higher priority than addition so the meaning is the same as 4+(5/7). Where priorities are equal, expressions are evaluated from left to right. Therefore 2/3*4 means the same as (2/3)*4 which could surprise the careless programmer! No two operators may appear in sequence so that 1+2−2 is not allowed, although 1+(−2) is permitted. In fact, any expression can be preceded by a + or −. This is because these quantities have a 'unary' meaning. i.e. −3 is a meaningful expression, but *3 is not.

The availability of brackets (parentheses) allows the programmer a convenient means of changing or specifying the order of evaluation or meaning of an expression. These must occur in pairs, meaning that every left bracket (open parentheses) must be matched by a later right bracket (close parentheses). Expressions within brackets are evaluated before the bracketed quantity is itself used.

EXERCISE   Experiment with the meaning of the following and other expressions using BASIC

$$4+5/7 \qquad 7/4*2/5 \qquad 3↑4↑5 \qquad 1+2↑3*4/5+6$$

It should be noted that in BASIC the operator * must always be explicitly stated, i.e. as 3*4. The expression (3)(4) which in normal mathematical notation implies a multiplication, is not recognized by BASIC.

8 BASIC Programs with Data Input—the INPUT statement

In order to be able to repeat similar calculations with different numbers, programming languages allow the actual numbers to be typed in when the program is run. This is done by the use of symbolic variables, much as in algebra, whose actual values can be requested by the running program. The INPUT statement accomplishes this in BASIC. The following example introduces the INPUT statement, and also shows the use of variables instead of numbers in arithmetic expressions:

```
10 INPUT A,B
20 PRINT (A+B)/2
30 END
```

When this program is run, it will reach line 10 and then require values for the variables A and B to be given before it can continue to line 20 where the average value of A and B is evaluated and printed. The request for the values of A and B is indicated by a prompting '?' which is typed on the terminal by the running program. When the request occurs, the desired numbers for A and B are typed in with a comma between, and finally 'carriage return' is typed. When two valid numbers have been entered, then the computer continues to line 20 where (A+B)/2 is evaluated and printed.

The flow chart which describes this program is shown in Fig. 1.2.

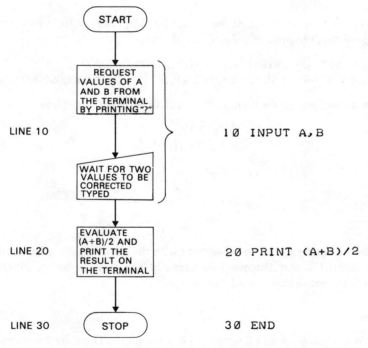

Fig. 1.2. Flow chart for a program to average two numbers.

Exactly two numbers are expected by the input statement at line 10. When the program is run and the '?' appears on the terminal, exactly two numbers should be typed in with a comma between. If the wrong number of values is entered, the computer will issue a self-explanatory message.

EXERCISE   Run this program, trying various values of A and B. Experiment with different expressions using more and fewer variables. Make deliberate typing errors, by entering too many or too few values.

It is possible to enter very large or very small numbers using a special 'exponential format' or E-format which is recognized by BASIC. A number can be represented in a form which gives a multiplying power of 10 such as 3×10^{10}. The exponential form is

$$n1En2$$

where $n1$ and $n2$ are numbers which may be signed and E is the letter E. This is interpreted as

$$n1 \times 10^{n2}$$

i.e. $n1$ times ten to the power $n2$. It will be found that BASIC prints results in exponential form if they are too large or small to print as ordinary numbers.

Examples   The BASIC form 3E1$0$ means 3×10^{10} or 30000000000
The BASIC form 2.4E−23 means 2.4×10^{-23} or 0.000000000000000000000024

Thus in response to the request for input in the previous program, the values
$$A = 3 \times 10^{10}$$
$$B = 2.4 \times 10^{-23}$$
could have been entered in the following manner:

? 3E1$0$,2.4E-23

EXERCISE   Use the same program to experiment with the use of exponential format. Enter numbers in exponential format. Discover how large a number must be before a PRINT statement presents the output in exponential format.

9 BASIC Variables

In the previous section variables A and B were used in an example. There are 286 variable names allowed by BASIC: the single letters A to Z, and the combinations of any single letter followed by any single number, such as A0, A1, . . . A9, B0, B1, . . . B9, etc.*

* Note that the letter O (oh) and the number 0 (zero) are easily confused. Which is intended is usually obvious, but it can be difficult to see when the wrong one has been used in error. A widespread practice for computer programs, adopted in this text for the programming examples, is to cross the number 0 (zero). Unfortunately the practice of crossing the letter O (oh) was once widely accepted and is still sometimes used.

10 Printing Captions

In a complicated program with many INPUT statements and many PRINT statements, it can be very confusing to interpret what a running program is doing unless explanatory messages appear. Therefore it is good practice both to print explanatory messages when input is desired and to use messages to identify results.

It has already been shown that a PRINT statement can evaluate and print any arithmetic expression, including single variable names. It is also possible to specify messages or strings of characters which are to be printed literally. Literal information is indicated by enclosing it in quotation marks. For example, the line

```
10 PRINT 5/7
```

produced a numeric answer in the first example of this session. The line

```
10 PRINT"5/7"
```

will give quite a different result.

EXERCISE   Try the program

```
10 PRINT "5/7 = "5/7
20 END
```

The above exercise will have demonstrated that several quantities can be printed in one PRINT statement, and that there can be either arithmetic expressions or character strings enclosed in quotation marks. Normally, expressions are separated by commas, as in the example

```
10 PRINT A,B,(A+B)/2
```

but it is not necessary to include the commas before or after literally stated character strings. The PRINT statement is further elaborated in Session 5.

EXERCISE   Try the program

```
10 PRINT "TYPE IN A AND B"
20 INPUT A,B
30 PRINT "A =" A "B =" B
40 PRINT "A+B)/2 =" (A+B)/2
50 END
```

whose flow diagram is shown in Fig. 1.3.

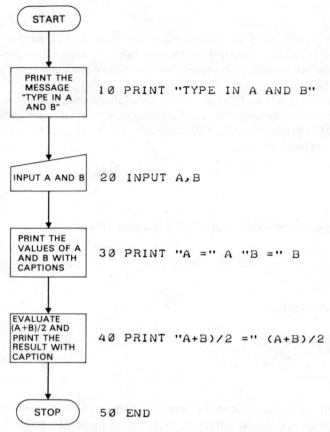

Fig. 1.3. Flow chart of a program to average two numbers with printing of captions.

11 Repeating Calculations—The GO TO statement

Another useful programming facility is the GO TO statement, which allows calculations to be repeated. The form of this is:

line number a **GO TO** *line number b*

The first line number is, of course, just the line number of the GO TO statement itself. When the GO TO statement is reached by a running program, the computer jumps to the specified place instead of continuing through the line numbers in sequence. Thus the statement at line 50

```
50 GO TO 10
```

causes the computer to jump to line 10 rather than carrying on to the next line number after 50.

Use of the GO TO statement can put a program in an endless loop, repeating the same calculation over and over. Such a program displays a flow chart with a closed pathway, or loop, as in the example:

```
10 PRINT "HERE GOES"
20 GO TO 20
30 END
```

with flow chart as shown in Fig. 1.4

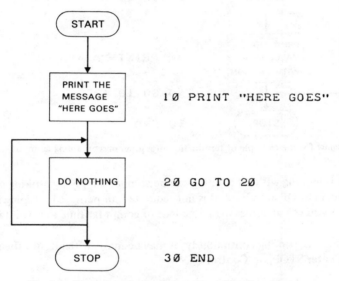

Fig. 1.4. Flow chart for program with endless closed loop.

The END statement in this example is never reached. This program should not be tried as it could very quickly waste a great deal of computer time.

There are several ways out of a loop situation. First of all, a program which contains an INPUT statement can be stopped by typing in STOP or possibly 'Control C' in place of the requested input.

EXERCISE   Try the following example, and terminate it by typing in STOP, or 'Control C'.

```
10 PRINT "TYPE IN A"
20 INPUT A
30 PRINT "A ="A
40 GO TO 10
50 END
```

The flow chart for this program is shown in Fig. 1.5.

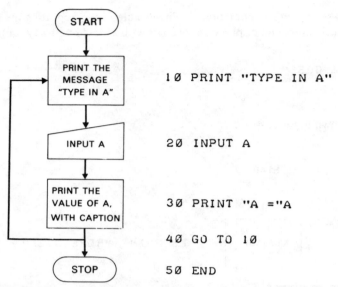

Fig. 1.5. Flow chart for the example of termination of a program containing an input statement.

A program which is looping without printing can be stopped simply by striking a key on the terminal, or by typing in STOP even if input is not requested, or perhaps by typing in 'Control C'.* Do not try this unless you can afford as many seconds of computer time as it will take you to stop it.

If a program in a loop is printing continuously, it may be more difficult, but the procedure is still to strike keys or enter STOP, or 'Control C'.

EXERCISE   Run and terminate the following example, whose flow chart is shown in Fig. 1.6.

```
10 PRINT "STOP ME"
20 GO TO 10
30 END
```

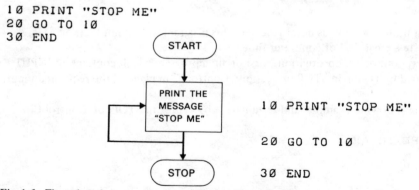

Fig. 1.6. Flow chart for example of termination of a program in an endless loop without an INPUT statement.

* The purpose of this section is to determine exactly what procedure does stop a running program because this can vary considerably between computers.

12 Problems

However simple a problem may seem, it is always worthwhile preparing a flow chart and writing the solution out by hand before attempting it on the computer. It is good practice to give messages which explain the quantity and purpose of input data before it is requested, and printed output should be accompanied by explanations as well.

PROBLEM 1.1   Write a program to square numbers entered one at a time.

Solution   Let variable X7 be used for the number. X7 must then be requested by an INPUT statement and squared in a PRINT statement. A GO TO statement returns to request more input. A possible program is given below, whose flow diagram is shown in Fig. 1.7.

```
10    PRINT "TYPE IN A SINGLE NUMBER TO OBTAIN ITS SQUARE"
20    INPUT X7
30    PRINT X7"SQUARED ="X7↑2
40    GO TO 20
50    END
```

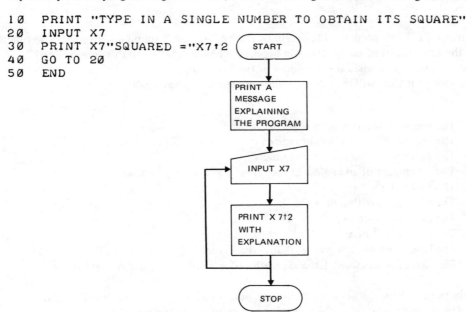

Fig. 1.7. **A possible solution to Problem 1.1.**

PROBLEM 1.2   Use a solution of problem 1.1 to find the square root of 63 to three significant figures.

PROBLEM 1.3   Write a program which calculates the average speed of a journey, by typing in both the distance in suitable units and the total elapsed time in hours, minutes, and seconds. The average speed is obviously just the distance divided by the elapsed time. However the time used must first be converted entirely to one variable as hours or minutes or seconds.

PROBLEM 1.4   Write a program which calculates the gross return r on compound interest, which is
$$r = (1 + i/100)^n$$
where i = interest rate per period, in %
       n = number of periods

Using this program find the number of periods taken to at least double an investment at 4%, 6%, 8%.

13 Library Functions in BASIC

The calculating power of most computer languages is greatly enhanced by the provision of library functions which evaluate often-used functions. For example in BASIC the SQR function finds square roots, and may be used as part of any arithmetic expression. The following program uses SQR to find the hypotenuse of a right angled triangle, given the other two sides:

```
10 PRINT"THIS PROGRAM FINDS THE HYPOTENUSE"
20 PRINT"TYPE IN TWO SIDES"
30 INPUT A,B
40 PRINT "HYPOTENUSE ="SQR(A↑2+B↑2)
50 GO TO 20
60 END
```

In statement 40 of this program, the length of the hypotenuse is found and printed. The function SQR finds the square root of the quantity in brackets which follows it, in this case A↑2+B↑2. This bracketed quantity is called the argument of the function.

Most versions of BASIC will include the following mathematical functions:

Function	Meaning
SIN(x)	The sine of x where x is an angle in radians
COS(x)	The cosine of x where x is in radians
TAN(x)	The tangent of x where x is in radians
ATN(x)	The arctangent of an angle x in the range $-\pi/2$ to $+\pi/2$ radians
EXP(x)	The value of e^x
LOG(x)	The natural logarithm of x
ABS(x)	The absolute value of x
SQR(x)	The square root of x
INT(x)	The largest integer not greater than x. Example: INT(5.95)=5 and INT(-5.95)=-6
SGN(x)	The sign of x, has value 1 if x is positive; 0 if x is 0; or -1 if x is negative

In the above functions, x represents any expression, which may of course include other functions. The quantity x is called the argument or parameter of the function.

A function RND, which is a random number generator, appears in most versions of BASIC, and is used in various supplementary problems throughout this book.

14 Problems

PROBLEM 1.5   Given two positive integers, find their quotient, the integer part of their quotient, and the remainder after integer division.

Example   suppose the quotient is 22/7, or 3.142857... (which in computer terms is not very close to π). The integer part of this quotient is 3, and the remainder is 1 (not 1/7), as in the division:

$$
\begin{array}{r}
3 \quad \longleftarrow \text{ integer part of quotient} \\
7 \overline{)2\,2} \\
2\,1 \\
\hline
1 \quad \longleftarrow \text{ remainder}
\end{array}
$$

Solution   let the numbers be N and D, then the quotient is N/D and in BASIC the integer part of the quotient is INT(N/D). The remainder can be found as the difference between N and D∗INT(N/D), as the example shows. Thus a suitable program is as shown in Fig. 1.8.

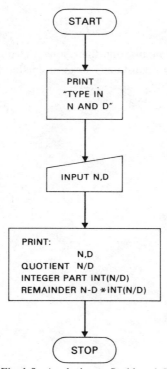

Fig. 1.8. A solution to Problem 1.5.

Complete the solution by programming it in BASIC.

PROBLEM 1.6   Calculate the value of π with the ATN function, using the fact that tan $\pi/4$ = 1

PROBLEM 1.7   Given the two sides adjacent to the right angle in a triangle, calculate the length of the hypotenuse and find the other two angles in degrees. Use the expression for π (not its value) found in problem 1.6.

PROBLEM 1.8   The period T seconds of a pendulum of length l metres for a small angle of swing is

$$T = 2\pi\sqrt{l/g}$$

where g = 9.81 metres/sec^2
(a) Write a program to find the period from the length.
(b) Write a program to find the length from the period.

PROBLEM 1.9   Suppose the time of day is given as a decimal number in hours, for example 18.5 is 18 hours, 30 minutes, no seconds. Write a program which converts the given time to hours, minutes, and seconds.

PROBLEM 1.10   The resonant frequency of an *LC* network is given by

$$\frac{1}{2\pi\sqrt{LC}} \text{ Hz}$$

Given *L* and *C* in henries and farads, find the resonant frequency. Sensible values for *L* and *C* are usually in millihenries and microfarads, or even smaller. Therefore, use exponential data format in entering sensible values.

15 Summary Notes on Session 1

(a) BASIC statements take the form

line number statement

(b) BASIC statements are entered by typing them into the terminal, ending the line with 'carriage return'.

(c) BASIC statements are corrected by typing in the corrected statement in full.

(d) BASIC statements are inserted by typing in the new statement with an appropriate line number.

(e) BASIC statements may be deleted by typing in the line number and 'carriage return', without intervening blanks.

(f) BASIC programs can be printed on the terminal with the LIST command.

(g) BASIC programs are run by the RUN command.

(h) BASIC programs are obeyed in order of line number.

(i) BASIC variable names:

any letter or any letter plus a single number

$$A \text{ to } Z$$
$$A\emptyset \text{ to } Z\emptyset$$
$$.$$
$$.$$
$$.$$
$$A9 \text{ to } Z9$$

(j) BASIC arithmetic uses the hierarchy

( )	expressions in brackets	high priority
↑	exponentiation	
*∕	multiplication and division	
+ −	addition and subtraction	low priority

Pairs of brackets (parentheses) clarify the priority.
Operations of equal priority are performed from left to right.

(k) the PRINT statement:

line number **PRINT** *quantity, quantity, ...*

where *quantity* can be a BASIC arithmetic expression (single variables are valid) or a character string enclosed in quotation marks.
More information about PRINT is given in Session 5.

(l) the INPUT statement:

line number **INPUT** *variable, variable, ...*

a running program types the prompt '?' to request input.
Type in numbers separated by commas, or type in STOP.
Data can be in exponential format, i.e.
$.1E-\emptyset5$ means 10^{-6}.

(m) the GO TO statement:

line number a **GO TO** *line number b*

when *line number a* is reached an unconditional program jump to *line number b* occurs.

(n) the END statement:

line number **END**

an END statement must be the highest numbered line of any BASIC program. When it is encountered a running program terminates.

(o) Library functions in BASIC

A number of standard functions are included in BASIC; some are listed in section 13 of this session. Functions operate on their arguments given within brackets after the function name, which can be expressions of any complexity including other functions.

Example

```
LOG(1/SQR(1-X↑2))
```

finds the natural logarithm of the reciprocal of the square root of one minus X squared, which presumes $X < 1$.

16 Supplementary Problems

PROBLEM 1.10   The integer part of the quotient and remainder as found in problem 1.5 can be used to convert decimal numbers into other bases using successive division by the base.
Find 33 to base 7, 600 to base 6
  32767 to base 5, 100 to base 8

PROBLEM 1.11   (a) Write a program which finds the square root of a number x, but which will give the answer $-\sqrt{x}$ if x is negative. (b) Write a program which finds the square root of a number but gives the answer 0 if x is negative. Hint: use the SGN function twice.

PROBLEM 1.12   Using functions from section 13 of this session, find the arcsine and arccosine of an angle given in degrees.

PROBLEM 1.13   Write a program to provide truncation of a number to its integer part. (This is not the same as the INT function.)

Examples   5.5 truncated becomes 5
       -5.5 truncated becomes -5

PROBLEM 1.14   The Newton–Raphson iteration is a popular means of finding the roots of equations of the form $f(x) = 0$. It is based on the simple geometrical notion that if a crude estimate x_0 of the solution is known, then an improved estimate x_1 can be found using the slope $f'(x_0)$, as in Fig. 1.9.

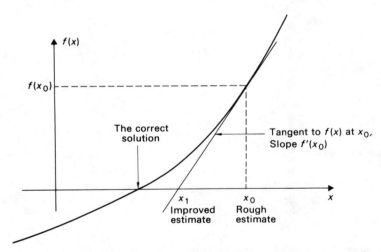

Fig. 1.9. Illustrating the Newton–Raphson method.

From this diagram, the slope of the tangent at x_0 can be found as

$$f'(x_0) = \frac{f(x_0)}{x_0 - x_1}$$

from which

$$x_1 = x_0 - \frac{f(x_0)}{f'(x_0)}$$

If the first guess of x_0 is good enough, successive use of this equation will quickly lead to the correct answer. Write a program to find a better estimate of the square root of a number c by applying the Newton–Raphson method to the equation $x^2 - c = 0$. By re-entering each improved guess the square root can be found. Find $\sqrt{2}$, $\sqrt{10}$, and $\sqrt{4096}$ in this way.

PROBLEM 1.15.   The function RND can be used to generate a series of numbers that appear to be random, and are called pseudorandom. These numbers are evenly distributed between 0 and 1. Write a program which uses the random number generator to simulate the tossing of a coin. Toss the simulated coin 20 times and count the number of heads and tails produced. It is likely that the number of heads and tails is not the same. How significant is this? Note: The form of the RND function is itself somewhat random. The recently published Specification for Standard BASIC gives it as having no argument, but in many implementations it has one. To compound the confusion the argument, if it is necessary, is sometimes meaningless.

SESSION 2
DECISIONS IN BASIC

1 Introduction

This session introduces two powerful and fundamental facilities common to all high level computing languages. These are the ability to form new variables and assign values to them, and the means of comparing or testing quantities to decide the course of the calculation. The Newton–Raphson iteration is used as an example in which a number of important programming principles are discussed.

The LET statement allows variables to have values assigned to them based on expressions involving other variables. This assignment or replacement facility in some programming languages tends to confuse the novice because the statements seem to imply contradictory mathematical situations. However the LET statement of BASIC avoids this problem by being self-explanatory.

The means of testing or comparing quantities is provided by relational expressions in which the truth or falsehood of a mathematical relationship can be found. Decisions based on these relationships can then be taken by the IF . . . THEN statement of BASIC.

This is the most important session for the beginner, and it is therefore worth extra effort in its completion. Using the material of this session, virtually any numerical problem could be attempted. The sessions which follow introduce facilities which add great convenience, but those presented here are the foundation of all computer programming.

2 Assignment of Values to Variables . . . the LET statement

In Session 1, arithmetic expressions were used only in PRINT statements. If all calculations were so restricted, a programming language would be virtually useless. Accordingly all computer languages include assignment or replacement facilities providing the advantages of calculating and storing intermediate results. The LET statement of BASIC is available for this purpose.

The following is an example of a LET statement:

```
30 LET D = B↑2-4*A*C
```

This is easily recognized as the calculation of the discriminant $b^2 - 4ac$ of the quadratic equation $ax^2 + bx + c = 0$. This LET statement evaluates the expression using known values of A, B, and C on the right hand side and assigns its value to the new variable D on the left of the equals sign.

The general form of a LET statement is:

line number **LET** *variable = expression*

When a LET statement is encountered in a running BASIC program, the expression on the right hand side is evaluated. The result then replaces the previous value (if any) of the variable on the left hand side. Thus the effect of a LET statement is to assign a value to the variable on the left hand side. LET statements are sometimes called assignment or replacement statements. The expression on the right hand side must obviously contain only variables whose own values have been determined earlier in the program.

Example   In problem 1.5, a quotient, its integer part, and its remainder were found. The use of LET statements will eliminate the repetition of some expressions in the solution which was given, and make the program more efficient. Suppose variables N and D are used to form the quotient as before. This time, let a variable Q be used for the quotient N/D, I for the integer part of the quotient, and R for the remainder.

The program and flow chart could then be as shown in Fig. 2.1.

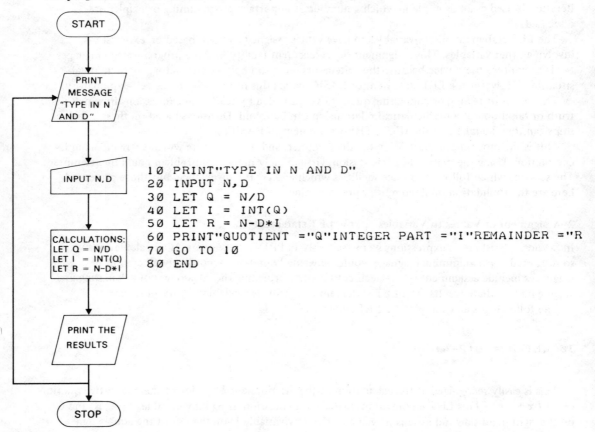

```
10  PRINT"TYPE IN N AND D"
20  INPUT N,D
30  LET Q = N/D
40  LET I = INT(Q)
50  LET R = N-D*I
60  PRINT"QUOTIENT ="Q"INTEGER PART ="I"REMAINDER ="R
70  GO TO 10
80  END
```

Fig. 2.1. A program for finding the quotient of two numbers along with the integer part of the quotient and the remainder.

EXERCISE   Try this program which, though longer, is more efficient.

3 Self-Replacement in LET Statements

A very important use of the LET statement is in the self-replacement of a previously used variable. At first glance, the following statement might seem contradictory:

55 LET I = I+1

However, consideration of the operation of the LET statement reveals that this is perfectly valid. The statement calls for the variable I to be replaced by its old value plus one, i.e. variable I is incremented by one.

Example   Self-replacement can be used to generate all the powers of 2 in a single variable x. Starting with $x = 1$, successive doubling is performed, so that x obeys a recurrence relationship

$$x_{new} = 2x_{old}$$

The program is as shown in Fig. 2.2

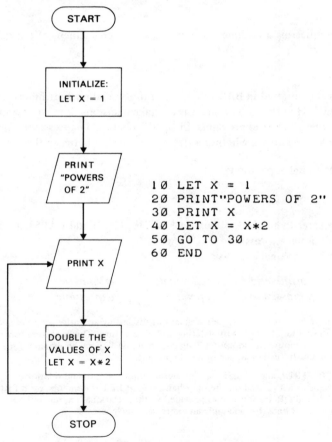

```
10 LET X = 1
20 PRINT"POWERS OF 2"
30 PRINT X
40 LET X = X*2
50 GO TO 30
60 END
```

Fig. 2.2. A program illustrating self-replacement.

The first time line 30 is reached, x has the value 1, or 2^0. Subsequently x is doubled on every repetition of the loop, so that when the program reaches line 30 for the nth time, x has the value 2^{n-1}.

4 Problems*

These problems, which appeared in Session 1, can be solved more efficiently using the LET statement. In each the same expression will have appeared more than once, and would therefore have required the computer to repeat the evaluation unnecessarily.

PROBLEM 2.1.   Given the two sides adjacent to the right angle of a triangle, calculate the length of the hypotenuse and find the other two angles in degrees. A LET statement should be used to define π using the ATN function (see problem 1.6).

PROBLEM 2.2   Suppose the time of day is given as a decimal number in hours, for example 18.5 is 18 hours, 30 minutes, no seconds. Write a program to convert the given time to hours, minutes, and seconds.

PROBLEM 2.3   After requesting a variable x as input, use self-replacement of a variable T to generate $1, x, x^2, x^3 \ldots$

5 Relational Expressions

So far the expressions encountered in BASIC have been those of simple arithmetic, involving the operations $+, -, *, /$, and $\uparrow$. However if a program is to make decisions, it must in some way make comparisons between quantities or expressions. In BASIC relational expressions can be written, which compare two quantities to see whether a stated relationship between them is TRUE or FALSE.

For example the relational expression:

```
A > 1 Ø * B
```

will be TRUE if A is greater than 1Ø*B, otherwise FALSE. TRUE and FALSE are the only possible results of a relational expression.†

The general form of a relational expression is:

arithmetic	*relational*	*arithmetic*
expression	*operator*	*expression*

* By this stage, it should have been realized that some means of discarding an entire program and starting afresh with a new one would be desirable, other than by deleting each line in turn. This is accomplished by a system command, which varies from computer to computer. The command NEW is recommended for standard BASIC; if it does not apply then obviously further advice should be sought.

† In some versions of BASIC, TRUE and FALSE have numeric values 1 and 0, and relational expressions can form part of other expressions, such as used on the right hand side of LET statements, or in PRINT statements. Additionally operators AND and OR are sometimes provided so that relational expressions can then be more complicated than those presented here. For example an expression such as

```
( A > B * 1 Ø ) O R ( C < = 1 )
```

might be encountered.

Thus any two arithmetic expressions can be related. The available relational operators are:*

$$
\begin{array}{ll}
= & \text{equal to} \\
> & \text{greater than} \\
< & \text{less than} \\
> = \text{ or } = > & \text{greater or equal} \\
< = \text{ or } = < & \text{less or equal} \\
<> \text{ or } >< & \text{not equal}
\end{array}
$$

Examples $10 > 10$ is FALSE
$10 = 10$ is TRUE
$5 < = 6$ is TRUE
$A = B$ is TRUE if A equals B, otherwise FALSE
$\left.\begin{array}{l} B^2 - 4*A*C > 0 \\ B^2 - 4*A*C = 0 \\ B^2 - 4*A*C < 0 \end{array}\right\}$ only one of these can be TRUE

6 Making Decisions—the IF . . . THEN statement and a problem

Relational expressions are used in the IF . . . THEN statement to determine or alter the course of a running BASIC program. The IF . . . THEN statement takes the form:

line number a **IF** $\dfrac{relational}{expression}$ **THEN** *line number b*

When an IF . . . THEN statement is encountered a decision is made about which line is to be obeyed next. If this *relational expression* is TRUE, then execution jumps to *line number b* as if a GO TO *line number b* statement had occurred. If the relational expression is FALSE, then the next line to be executed will be the one which naturally follows in sequence after *line number a*.

Example

```
20  IF I=10 THEN 50
30
40
50
```

In this example, when execution reaches line 20, the value of I is compared to 10. If I = 0, then the next statement reached is line 50. Otherwise the program continues in the usual sequence by proceeding to line 30. Thus a means of skipping directly to line 50 has been provided if I = 10 at line 20.

Example   Suppose a program is to be written which finds the square root of a number Z entered at the terminal, but the input is not to be accepted if it is negative. An IF . . . THEN statement could be used to check that the entered number is correct. The program shown in Fig. 2.3 would suffice.

* Even if the keys $\geqslant$, $\leqslant$ or $\neq$ are present on the terminal the long forms $> =$ or $= >$, $< =$ or $= <$, and $<>$ or $><$ must be used.

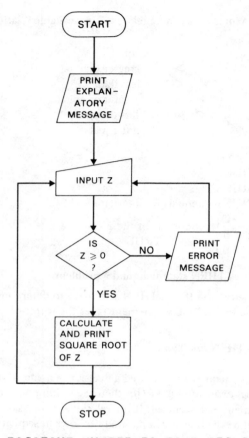

Fig. 2.3. A program demonstrating the IF . . . THEN statement.

```
10 PRINT"TYPE IN A POSITIVE NUMBER TO FIND ITS SQUARE ROOT"
20 INPUT Z
30 IF Z>=0 THEN 60
40 PRINT"THAT WAS NEGATIVE, TRY AGAIN"
50 GO TO 20
60 PRINT"SQUARE ROOT ="SQR(Z)
70 GO TO 20
80 END
```

The above example shows how the decision making facility complicates the flow of a program. A diamond shaped symbol is used in flow charts for decisions because the alternative program paths are easily connected to it. Fig. 2.4 shows the meaning of the various flow diagram shapes used in this text.

It should be noted that translation of the flow chart into a BASIC program could lead to several forms which are equivalent. It is best that the program should be straightforward, using as few

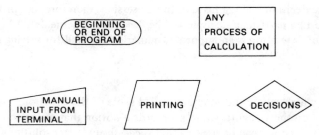

Fig. 2.4. Conventional symbols for flow charts.

jumps from place to place as possible. Two other translations of the same program are now given, one which is good and the other terrible, although both are described by the same flow chart, Fig. 2.3.

GOOD

```
10 PRINT"TYPE IN A POSITIVE NUMBER TO FIND ITS SQUARE ROOT"
20 INPUT Z
30 IF Z<0 THEN 60
40 PRINT"SQUARE ROOT ="SQR(Z)
50 GO TO 20
60 PRINT"THAT WAS NEGATIVE, TRY AGAIN"
70 GO TO 20
80 END
```

TERRIBLE

```
10 PRINT"TYPE IN A POSITIVE NUMBER TO FIND ITS SQUARE ROOT"
20 INPUT Z
30 IF Z<0 THEN 50
40 GO TO 70
50 PRINT"THAT WAS NEGATIVE, TRY AGAIN"
60 GO TO 80
70 PRINT"SQUARE ROOT ="SQR(Z)
80 GO TO 20
90 END
```

EXERCISE   Try one of the approved solutions in this example.

PROBLEM 2.4   In section 3 of this Session, a program was written as an example in which the powers of 2 were generated by self-replacement. Rewrite this program to stop after the number 1024 is printed.

7 A Numerical Method—the Newton-Raphson iteration

The facilities introduced by this session allow more interesting problems to be attempted than those presented earlier. The solutions to these problems will be more complicated in their structure because of the decision making feature. In this session, therefore, the programming considerations attached to a particular example will be described in some detail.

The Newton–Raphson interation is an important numerical method for solving equations of the form

$$f(x) = 0$$

to find real values of x which satisfy the equation, called roots of the equation.

This method is based on the straightforward geometrical notion that, using an original guess of the root, tangents to the function can be used to find successively better solutions. In Fig. 2.5, if x_n is a guess of the answer, then a tangent of slope $f'(x_n)$ can be drawn. The point where the tangent crosses the x-axis is then taken as an improved estimate of the answer, called x_{n+1}. The slope of the tangent can be found by differentiating $f(x)$, and also geometrically, as in

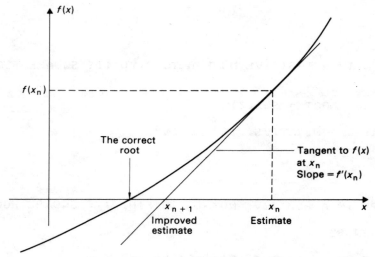

Fig. 2.5. The Newton–Raphson iteration.

Fig. 2.5, by

$$f'(x) = \frac{f(x_n)}{x_n - x_{n+1}}$$

from which

$$x_{n+1} = x_n - \frac{f(x_n)}{f'(x_n)} \tag{2.1}$$

The procedure for solving $f(x) = 0$ is to use equation 2.1 repeatedly, starting with an initial guess of the root and producing successively improved estimates of the answer. This is called the Newton–Raphson iteration, and is treated in detail by any good text on numerical methods. Under favourable conditions a rapid approach to the correct root is achieved, because this method has the desirable characteristic of quadratic convergence, which implies that as the method approaches the solution, the number of digits of accuracy is doubled with each stage of calculation.

8 Translating Procedures into Programs—flow diagrams

The Newton–Raphson method is not difficult to translate into a program, and certain principles of good programming practice can help to accomplish this easily. Once a mathematical definition of the procedure is achieved, a flow diagram should be prepared to represent the structure of the program graphically.

   This particular method involves an iteration using the recurrence relationship

$$x_{n+1} = x_n - \frac{f(x_n)}{f'(x_n)}$$

Such recurrence relationships always suggest the use of replacement statements to produce the recurrence in a single program loop. A flow chart for this method is given in Fig. 2.6.

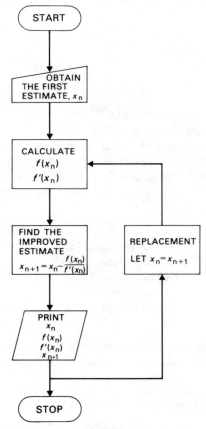

Fig. 2.6. Flow chart for the Newton–Raphson iteration. Note the use of replacement.

Particular note should be taken of the replacement of x_n by x_{n+1} in the return path of the iteration. This causes the improved estimate x_{n+1} to be used as the crude estimate x_n in the next stage and so further improved estimates are obtained automatically. As a matter of good practice, it should also be noticed that the programmer has decided to print the result of every calculation in the procedure. This is always worthwhile in developing and testing a new program. Errors in any program are likely to occur through programming mistakes, and usually cannot be traced without comprehensive information. Therefore a liberal spread of PRINT statements throughout a calculation is always valuable; redundant printing is easily removed once the procedure is fully tested.

9 Translating Programs into BASIC–the REM statement

Up to this point $f(x)$ has not been defined–it could be any function whose root is sought. As an example, suppose the equation to be solved is

$$f(x) = x^2 - 2 = 0$$

which has as solution

$$x = \pm \sqrt{2}$$

Then

$$f'(x) = 2x$$

gives the slope of the tangent at x, which is required for the method.

It is now very easy to translate the flow diagram into BASIC. First of all, suitable variable names must be chosen to represent the quantities used in the program. A common error is to choose an invalid name, such as F(X) for $f(x)$–this is completely wrong (and also dangerous, for reasons which cannot be appreciated until Session 7). It must be recalled that variable names can only be either a single letter such as F, or a letter followed by a number such as X1.

Suitable choices for this example could be

> F to represent $f(x)$
> P to represent $f'(x)$
> X∅ to represent x_n
> X1 to represent x_{n+1}
> C to represent c

With reference to the flow diagram, the program can be written out in BASIC by hand, and checked carefully before it is typed into the terminal and tried. The following is a possible solution:

```
1∅ PRINT"TYPE IN AN ESTIMATE OF SQR(2)"
2∅ INPUT X∅
3∅ LET F=X∅↑2-2
```

```
40 LET P=2*X0
50 LET X1=X0-F/P
60 PRINT"AT "X0"F(X) IS "F"SLOPE "P"NEW ESTIMATE "X1
70 LET X0=X1
80 GO TO 30
90 END
```

Hopefully the reader has been able to follow this discussion and can understand the above program. However it is obvious that it does not explain itself, as ideally any program should. A program of any complexity should include generous numbers of comments or remarks which explain its operation. This is accomplished using the REM statement whose form is

line number **REM** *any remark or comment*

The REM statement is ignored when the program is run, but is always included in the program listing. The combination of a flow diagram and suitable remarks within a program makes it easy to understand. This is important even to the programmer himself who could return to his program after a long interval and be completely baffled by it.

The example of this section is therefore considerably improved by the addition of remarks:

```
10    REM CALCULATION OF SQR(2) BY NEWTON-RAPHSON ITERATION
20    REM BY SOLVING F(X) = X↑2-C = 0
30    REM FIRST ACCEPT AN ESTIMATE OF THE ANSWER
40    PRINT "TYPE IN AN ESTIMATE OF SQR(2)"
50    INPUT X0
60    REM CALCULATE F(X) AND ITS SLOPE
70    LET F=X0↑2-2
80    LET P=2*X0
90    REM NOW CALCULATE AN IMPROVED ESTIMATE X1
100   LET X1=X0-F/P
110   PRINT "AT "X0"F(X) IS "F"SLOPE "P"NEW ESTIMATE "X1
120   REM USE THE NEW ESTIMATE AS DATA FOR A NEW ITERATION
130   LET X0=X1
140   GOTO 70
150   END
```

10 Problems

PROBLEM 2.5   Rewrite the example of the previous section to find the square root of any number, entered through the terminal
Under what conditions are the positive or negative values found?

11 Stopping the Iteration Automatically—accuracy

The decision making ability of BASIC has not yet been applied to the Newton–Raphson method. It is difficult to predict in advance how many repetitions of the iteration will be needed to produce an answer of particular accuracy. Given a suitable starting value, the calculation will approach the true root of $f(x) = 0$, but it is unlikely that it will ever actually reach it, because a computer has a limited number of digits of accuracy and therefore introduces its own 'round off' errors into the calculation. For example in trying to find the solution to:

$$x^2 - c = 0$$

the square root of c is sought. If $c = 2$, then the answer $\sqrt{2}$ is irrational, and contains an infinite number of non-repeating digits. This answer could never be found exactly because it cannot be represented by a finite number of digits.

Therefore the problem of finding when the calculation is close enough to the answer arises. A 'stopping criterion' must be found which can be used to halt the iteration when the answer is good enough. This is where the decision making feature of BASIC enters into this problem, and similar problems. A suitable stopping criterion depends on the desired accuracy, the resolution of the computer, the characteristics of the numerical procedure, or all three. It is absurd to ask for more digits of accuracy than the computer can potentially present, and it is generally not possible to achieve the full resolution of the computer without some error. The usual practice is to consider the amount by which the answer changes after each stage and stop the calculation when this is small enough.

However this is not as simple as it might seem, since in finding $\sqrt{2}$ one would probably desire greater absolute accuracy than in finding $\sqrt{210000000}$. Thus the relative accuracy is a more useful quantity on which to base the stopping criterion. In the Newton–Raphson iteration the absolute change is $x_{n+1} - x_n$, but a more suitable quantity is an error expression involving the normalized absolute value of the change:

$$E = \frac{x_{n+1} - x_n}{x_{n+1}}$$

This might fail, however, if the root itself were very small.

Finally, in seeking a particular accuracy the convergence characteristic of the method used must be considered. In the Newton–Raphson method, quadratic convergence is achieved, and so when the method is close to the answer, the number of digits of accuracy will be doubled by each iteration.

The quantity E provides a measure of the accuracy of solution, but it applies to the previous iteration. That is, E is an approximation to the error in x_n. Near the correct root, the error in x_{n+1} will be of the order of E^2 because of quadratic convergence. Therefore it is a waste of computer resources to carry on the calculation until E is smaller than the desired error, because x_{n+1} will have twice the number of digits required. If an error of 1 part in 10^6 is sought, then it is likely to be achieved when E is less than 10^{-3}, or 10^{-4} to provide some margin of safety.

Suppose the Newton–Raphson technique is to be used to solve an equation $f(x) = 0$, and the answer is to be accepted when the normalized difference between successive estimates is less than 10^{-4}, implying a normalized error close to 10^{-8}. Then a suitable flow diagram is as shown in Fig. 2.7.

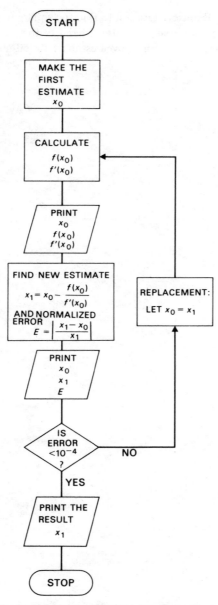

Fig. 2.7. Flow diagram for Newton–Raphson iteration with stopping condition.

12 Problems

PROBLEM 2.6   Use the Newton–Raphson iteration to find the square root of a number to 1 part in 10^5. Instead of asking for an initial guess, use either 1 or the number itself. (The first iteration will always produce the same improved estimate for either of these choices.)

13 Summary Notes on Session 2

(a) the LET statement:

line number **LET** *variable = expression*

The expression on the right hand side (which could just be a variable name) is evaluated, and the result replaces the variable on the left hand side. The expression can only contain known variables.

(b) Relational Expressions:

arithmetic	*relational*	*arithmetic*
expression	*operator*	*expression*

example: A > B

The result is TRUE or FALSE.

(c) Relational Operators:
The available relational operators are:

$$
\begin{array}{ll}
= & \text{equal to} \\
> & \text{greater than} \\
< & \text{less than} \\
>= \text{ or } => & \text{greater or equal} \\
<= \text{ or } =< & \text{less or equal} \\
<> \text{ or } >< & \text{not equal}
\end{array}
$$

(d) The IF . . . THEN statement:

line number a **IF** *relational expression* **THEN** *line number b*

If the *relational expression* is TRUE, then the program jumps to *line number b*. Otherwise the program continues in the normal sequence.

(e) The REM statement:

line number **REM** *any remark*

This has no effect in a running program.

14 Supplementary Problems

PROBLEM 2.7.   Find the roots of the quadratic equation $ax^2 + bx + c = 0$ by testing the discriminant and printing the appropriate results for each of the three possible cases.

PROBLEM 2.8   Using the Newton–Raphson iteration, find the nth root of any number to 1 part in 10^5.

PROBLEM 2.9   Using the Newton–Raphson iteration, find the real root of the equation, $x^3 - 7.8x^2 + 18.5x - 11.3 = 0$. If the initial guess is too large the root will be missed. Why?

PROBLEM 2.10   Write a program to find all the roots of a cubic equation $ax^3 + bx^2 + cx + d = 0$ using the Newton–Raphson iteration to locate one real root, and the general expression for quadratic equations to extract the remaining two roots.

PROBLEM 2.11   A method for iterative solution of the roots of equation which will always converge is called the method of False Position, or Regula Falsi. This method requires two initial points which are on either side of the root, and operates as shown in Fig. 2.8.

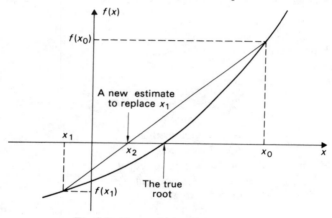

Fig. 2.8. The method of False Position.

x_0 and x_1 are guesses of the root which lie on either side of it, so that $f(x_0)$ is positive and $f(x_1)$ is negative. The new estimate x_2 lies at the intersection of the secant joining the two guesses and the x-axis. Thus

$$x_2 = x_0 - \frac{x_0 - x_1}{f(x_n) - f(x_1)} f(x_0)$$

The new estimate x_2 will be on one side or the other of the true root, and replaces whichever of x_0 and x_1 is on the same side of the root. Thus in the diagram

$$\text{if } f(x_2) > 0, \qquad x_2 \text{ replaces } x_0$$
$$\text{if } f(x_2) < 0, \qquad x_2 \text{ replaces } x_1$$

Write a program to extract the real root of

$$x^3 - 7.8x^2 + 18.5x - 11.3 = 0$$

using this method. How does its rate of convergence compare with that of the Newton–Raphson method? Can initial guesses be found for which it does not converge? Does it really matter which side of the root the initial guesses are?

SESSION 3
PROGRAM LOOPS

1 Introduction

The Newton–Raphson iteration which was studied in the previous session led to a program with the same calculation repeated until the method converged upon an acceptable answer. The number of repetitions was not predetermined, nor was the program made to count them. However, the repetition of these calculations formed a closed program loop, as the flow diagrams show. Many other computer applications involve repeated calculations, and often the number of repetitions is fixed, or must be counted. In this session the use of the IF . . . THEN statement to control looping is introduced and a number of problems are presented. The emphasis placed on good programming style is continued here with a discussion of series calculations and the use of recurrence relationships to improve program efficiency.

It will be found later that simpler means exist for controlling loops in BASIC. However, the purpose of this session is to provide important experience in the application of the fundamentals already presented.

2 Repeating Calculations

Digital computing procedures, or algorithms frequently require calculations to be repeated a certain number of times. This is an important form of program looping, so called because in the flow diagram for such a procedure, a closed path appears. Loops can be set up and controlled using LET statements for initialization and counting, and an IF . . . THEN statement to test for completion of the count, and so control the number of times it is repeated. Initialization, counting and testing are the elements of this kind of repetition.

Suppose a calculation is to be repeated 10 times. Then a variable I could be set aside to count the number of times the loop has been executed. Before the loop is entered, I is initialized by being set to one. Each time the end of the loop is reached I is incremented by one and then tested to see if the loop is complete. In this example the loop is repeated until I is greater than 10, when the program carries on to the next lines of calculation. Fig. 3.1 shows a typical flow diagram for looping.

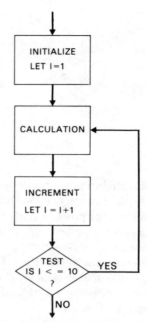

Fig. 3.1. A flow diagram of a loop repeated 10 times.

The program segment corresponding to Fig. 3.1 is:

```
60 REM INITIALIZE THE LOOP COUNTER
70 LET I = 1
80 REM THE REPEATED CALCULATION FOLLOWS
90
100
110
120
130        CALCULATION
140
150
160
170 REM INCREMENT THE LOOP COUNTER
180 LET I = I+1
190 REM TEST FOR LOOP COUNT COMPLETION
200 IF I<=10 THEN 90
```

Example   Problem 2.3 called for a variable x to be typed in, and for the terms $1, x, x^2, x^3 \ldots$ to be generated by self-replacement of a variable T. Suppose only the first ten of these quantities are desired, from x^0 to x^9. A variable J can be set aside to count the number of powers of x generated as shown in Fig. 3.2.

Note that the variable J is not actually included in the calculation, although it could have been; the term x^j could have been found as X↑J. This, however, would not have been efficient because computers take a great deal more time to exponentiate than they do to multiply.

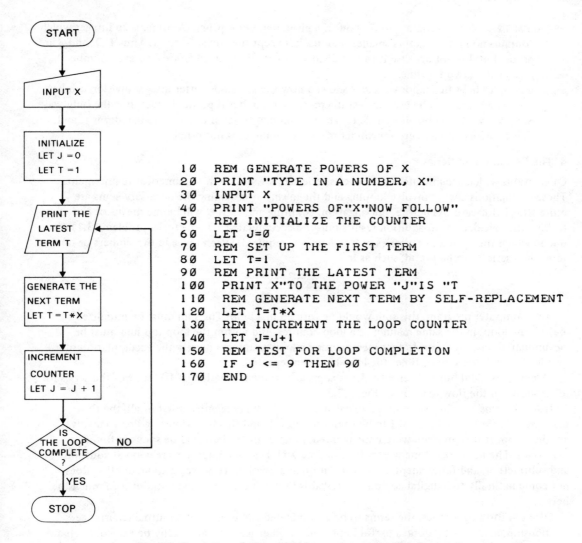

```
10    REM GENERATE POWERS OF X
20    PRINT "TYPE IN A NUMBER, X"
30    INPUT X
40    PRINT "POWERS OF"X"NOW FOLLOW"
50    REM INITIALIZE THE COUNTER
60    LET J=0
70    REM SET UP THE FIRST TERM
80    LET T=1
90    REM PRINT THE LATEST TERM
100   PRINT X"TO THE POWER "J"IS "T
110   REM GENERATE NEXT TERM BY SELF-REPLACEMENT
120   LET T=T*X
130   REM INCREMENT THE LOOP COUNTER
140   LET J=J+1
150   REM TEST FOR LOOP COMPLETION
160   IF J <= 9 THEN 90
170   END
```

Fig. 3.2. Generation of 10 powers of a number using self-replacement.

3 Problems

PROBLEM 3.1   Write a program to evaluate the factorial of a positive integer number. Find out how large a factorial the computer can manage by having the program try factorials of 1, 2, 4, 8, 16 . . . The factorial of an integer is called $n!$ or $\lfloor n$, and is the product of itself and all the positive integers smaller than itself:

$$n! = n(n - 1)(n - 2) \ldots 1$$
$$\text{Thus } 5! = (5)(4)(3)(2)(1) = 120$$
$$0! \text{ is defined to be } 1$$

PROBLEM 3.2   Write a program to find out if a given number is prime. A prime is an integer which contains no integer factors smaller than itself, except the trivial factor 1. Thus 1, 2, and 3 are prime, but 4 is not because it can be divided exactly by two. Obviously no even number greater than two is prime.

Examples in both Sessions 1 and 2 showed how the remainder after integer division can be calculated. This can be used to test if a particular number is prime. In fact, it is the only way. Simply try all possible integer factors of the number to see if any zero remainder is found. The existence of any zero remainder means the number is not prime.

4 The Evaluation of Series

Calculations which accumulate results over a series are a very common numerical requirement. These calculations always involve looping and the means of obtaining the necessary sums are quite straightforward. As before, initialization, counting and testing will be the means of controlling the calculation. In addition results must be accumulated. The factorial problem (3.1) was one in which the product of a series of numbers was required. Often the sum of numbers or of terms in a series is to be found, such as in

$$e^x = 1 + x + \frac{x^2}{2!} + \frac{x^3}{3!} + \cdots$$

In a computer program, this sum would be formed in a loop. The sum must be initialized before the loop, in the same manner as a loop counter, and within the loop the sum must be accumulated term by term. In fact incrementing a loop counter is merely the accumulation of a particular sum—the sum of times the loop has been repeated.

A perfectly valid but not terribly clever approach to the evaluation of 10 terms of the series for e^x is shown in the flow diagram of Fig. 3.3.

However, this algorithm includes two calculations which are lengthy. First of all, the flow diagram calls for the factorial of I to be found for each I, and this is obviously going to involve another loop. If this program were implemented, most of the time would be spent in finding factorial I. The next great time-waster is in finding X↑I. Digital computers are good at addition and subtraction, and fairly adept at multiplication and division. However, exponentiation does not come naturally to a digital computer, so if this problem can be solved without it so much the better.

Often in forming a series, the terms to be accumulated can be simplified into a recurrence relationship, and if this is done a useful improvement in efficiency can usually be gained. Such a relationship will always suggest a self-replacement statement for the generation of the terms in the series.

As it turns out, a recurrence relationship exists in the power series for e^x,

$$e^x = 1 + x + \frac{x^2}{2!} + \frac{x^3}{3!} + \cdots$$

which makes both the factorial and exponentiation unnecessary. Suppose the initial constant 1 is called term 0 of the series. Then term n, called T_n, is

$$T_n = \frac{x}{n} T_{n-1}$$

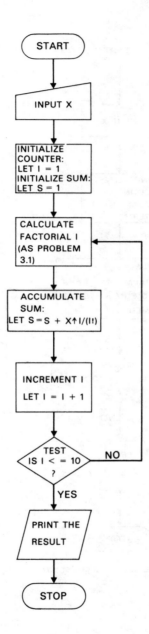

Fig. 3.3. Flow diagram of an inefficient program for summing the power series for e^x.

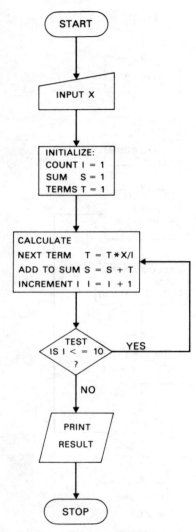

Fig. 3.4. Improved flow diagram for evaluation of e^x by a power series, using a recurrence relationship for efficiency.

Therefore, if the previous term T_{n-1} is known, the present term T_n is found by only one multiplication and one division. To achieve this, it is necessary only to set aside a variable T to hold the previous term and generate successive terms by self-replacement, as in the improved flow diagram, Fig. 3.4.

In this example, the efficiency of the calculation has been increased enormously by the recurrence relationship. In a series calculation the possibility of a recurrence should always be explored.

5 Problems

PROBLEM 3.3   Evaluate 10 terms of the power series for e^x:

$$e^x = 1 + x + \frac{x^2}{2!} + \frac{x^3}{3!} + \cdots$$

PROBLEM 3.4   Evaluate the power series for e^x to 0.01% accuracy, counting the number of terms required.

$$e^x = 1 + x + \frac{x^2}{2!} + \frac{x^3}{3!} + \cdots$$

Consider carefully the question of a suitable stopping criterion. Compare the result with the value given by the EXP function.

PROBLEM 3.5   Evaluate the series for $1\backslash(1-x)$ (valid for $-1 < x < 1$) to 0.01% accuracy, counting the number of terms required.

$$\frac{1}{1-x} = 1 + x + x^2 + x^3 + \cdots$$

PROBLEM 3.6   Evaluate the power series for $\sin x$ to 0.01% accuracy, counting the number of terms required. Compare the result with the value given by the SIN function.

$$\sin x = x - \frac{x^3}{3!} + \frac{x^5}{5!} - \frac{x^7}{7!} + \cdots$$

6 Summary Notes on Session 3

(a) The form of a counting program loop is as shown in Fig. 3.5.

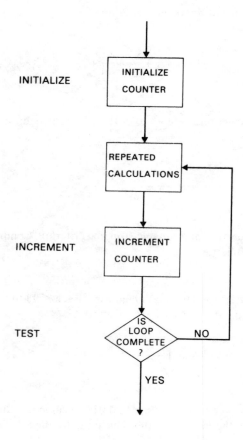

Fig. 3.5. Flow diagram for a counting program loop.

7 Supplementary Problems

PROBLEM 3.7   Over the range $-1 < x < 1$, e^x can be found by a polynomial

$$e^x = 1 + 1.000022x + 0.499199x^2 + 0.166488x^3 + 0.043794x^4 + 0.008687x^5$$

which is one of the type known as Chebyshev polynomials. Compare the accuracy of this polynomial with the use of 6 terms of the series

$$e^x = 1 + x + \frac{x^2}{2} + \frac{x^3}{6} + \frac{x^4}{24} + \frac{x^5}{120} + \cdots$$

PROBLEM 3.8.   Another method of finding e^x uses the continued fraction

$$e^x = 1 + \cfrac{x}{1 - \cfrac{x}{2 + \cfrac{x}{3 - \cfrac{x}{2 + \cfrac{x}{5 - \cfrac{x}{2 + \cfrac{x}{7 - \cfrac{x}{\text{etc.}}}}}}}}}$$

which in practice has to stop somewhere, because it would be programmed from the bottom up. Investigate the use of this formula as a means of finding e^x and compare with the previous methods.

PROBLEM 3.9   In many cases an analytic expression for the integrand of a function cannot be found, and such an integration can only be performed by an operation called numerical integration, or preferably numerical quadrature. One method, of many, is called the trapezoidal rule, in which

$$\int_{x_1}^{x_2} f(x) \, dx = \frac{f(x_1) + f(x_2)}{2(x_2 - x_1)}$$

which is simply the area of the shaded trapezoid in Fig. 3.6.

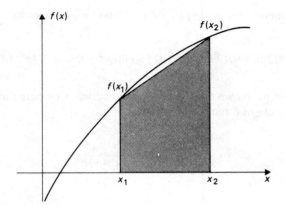

Fig. 3.6. Illustrating the trapezoidal rule.

Usually this would not be accurate enough for most integrations, so that in a practical situation a number of thin trapezoids would be taken and their areas summed.

Using the trapezoidal rule, find

$$\frac{1}{\sqrt{2\pi}} \int_0^1 e^{-x^2/2} \, dx$$

by dividing the range $0 \leqslant x \leqslant 1$ into ten equal segments and summing the areas of the trapezoids so formed.

SESSION 4
FURTHER MEANS OF PROGRAM CONTROL

1 Introduction

BASIC provides two further facilities for controlling the order in which statements are obeyed. The first of these involves the use of two statements, the FOR and NEXT statements, to delineate the beginning and end of program loops. Strictly speaking, this facility is not absolutely necessary, because looping can be controlled adequately using an IF . . . THEN statement. However the FOR and NEXT statements are nearly always used to control loops. This is because the FOR and NEXT statements express the requirements of looping in terms which are convenient to the programmer.

The other new means of program control is a single statement which provides for multiple decisions. The IF statement specifies only two possible outcomes designated by the truth or falsehood of a proposition. The ON . . . GO TO statement, on the other hand, can give a variety of program destinations. Although this facility is very useful when it is required, the need for it does not arise very often, so in practice it is not used as frequently as the IF . . . THEN statement.

These two facilities complete the BASIC repertoire of program control instructions. While both these features supplement the IF . . . THEN statement, it is noted that they are simply convenient tools which apply to particular situations. Both of their functions could be achieved using the IF . . . THEN statement.

2 A Convenient Means of Looping—the FOR and NEXT statements

In Session 3, program loops were controlled by initializing and incrementing a loop counter using the LET statement, and later testing for the completion of the loop using an IF . . . THEN statement. While this method is straightforward enough, it is not quite the way programmers think about loops. One would say 'I wish to perform the following calculation for I from 1 to 10', and this single statement of intention requires translation into three statements of BASIC. It would be much better to be able to write something like:

FOR I = 1 TO 10

Looping is such a common feature of computer programs that all high level programming languages have some means of automatically initializing, incrementing and testing loops. In BASIC, the FOR statement specifies all this information at the beginning of the loops, in much the same terms that a programmer would think of it. The end of the loop must be indicated, and the very simple NEXT statement does this. Therefore FOR and NEXT statements always occur in pairs.

For example, suppose a variable I is to be used to count 10 passes through a calculation. Then the FOR and NEXT statements would appear as follows

```
70 FOR I = 1 TO 10
80
90
100
110    CALCULATION
120
130
140
150 NEXT I
```

The great convenience of this method should be evident in the example. The FOR statement calls for the variable I to be used from 1 to 10, and the NEXT statement indicates where the next value of I is to be calculated and tested before the loop is repeated. In general the FOR statement specifies the variable name to be used as a loop counter, its initial value, and how much to increment it each time through the loop. The NEXT statement locates the end of the loop and states the variable name so that both programmer and computer are in no doubt about exactly which loop is being terminated.

Unless otherwise specified, the increment is always taken to be one. Therefore the preceding example provides a loop in which I takes the values $1, 2, 3, \ldots 10$ on successive turns through the calculation.

Step sizes other than 1 can be specified a longer form of the FOR statement, as in the following example:

```
65 FOR X = 0 TO 10 STEP .1
67
70
73    CALCULATION
75
77
80 NEXT X
```

Here the program lines between line 65 and line 80 will be repeated 101 times, with x taking the values $0, 0.1, 0.2, 0.3, \ldots 10.0$.

The FOR statement is very versatile because all three given quantities can be any expression; the starting value, the ending value, and the step size. Thus, for example, negative step sizes are possible.

Example   As a variation on an earlier program, suppose 9 powers of a number x are to be found in steps of 0.25 from 2 down to 0, i.e. $x^2, x^{1.75}, \ldots., 1$. This requirement can be met recursively using a variable A for the answers, and starting with $A = x^2$, the remaining values are generated by letting

$$A = A*x^{-1/4}$$

The program is

```
10 REM GENERATE POWERS OF 2 FROM 2 TO 0.25
20 REM REQUEST X
30 PRINT"TYPE IN X"
```

```
40 INPUT X
50 REM SET UP THE RECURSION FACTOR M
60 LET M = X↑(-0.25)
70 LET A = X*X
80 REM COUNT THROUGH THE DESIRED POWERS
90 FOR P = 2 TO .25 STEP -.25
100 PRINT X"TO POWER "P"IS "A
110 LET A = A*M
120 NEXT P
130 END
```

A flow chart for this program is given in Fig. 4.1. It should be noted that the variable M is assigned the value $x^{-1/4}$ before the loop begins. This improves program efficiency by removing

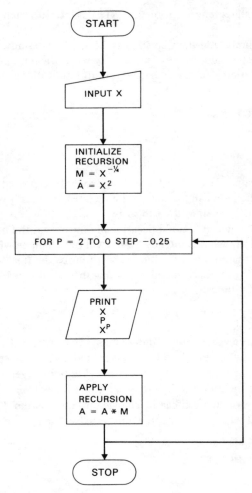

Fig. 4.1. Flow diagram for determination of some powers of a number using recurrence.

the calculation of $x^{-1/4}$ from the loop so that it is not repeated unnecessarily. It is good practice always to remove invariant expressions from program loops.

Note how the FOR . . . NEXT loop is still indicated by a return arrow although the increment and test are no longer explicitly indicated.

The general form of the FOR statement is:

line number **FOR** *variable* = *expression* **TO** *expression* **STEP** *expression.*

The meaning of the FOR . . . NEXT loop should be quite clear as the statements are both self explanatory. However careful thought would raise a number of questions of detail about its operation, and these are answered by the following set of rules:

(i) The STEP part of this statement is optional. If STEP is left out, then the step size is taken to be 1.

(ii) The upper and lower limits and the step size can be any expressions.

(iii) The initial, final and step values are evaluated only when the loop is begun, so that they cannot be changed while looping. This rule has important implications. Consider the following loop:

```
50 FOR I = J TO K STEP L
60 LET L = L*2
70 LET K = K-1
80 NEXT I
```

If J, K, and L had initial values 1, 10, and 1, this loop would be repeated 10 times. The changes made to L and K within the loop cannot change the number of times it is repeated.

(iv) Incrementing and testing occur at the end of the loop.

(v) Rounding errors in the computer could occasionally mean that the number of times the loop is repeated is not exactly what is intended. This will only happen when an accumulation of round off errors causes the intended final increment to miss the final value. Thus the programmer of the following FOR statement is running the risk that his loops may be repeated 3 rather than the intended 4 times:

```
150 FOR I = 0 TO 1 STEP 1/3
```

The expression 1/3 has a true value with infinitely many digits which the computer can only approximate. In some computers the third increment could produce a result slightly greater than 1 so the fourth repetition is missed. When dealing with noninteger expressions one should be careful about expecting the loop variable to hit an exact final value.

(vi) the value of the loop variable itself can be changed inside the loop. Each time the NEXT statement is encountered it will be incremented and tested in the normal way. Consider the following

```
50 FOR I = 1 TO 10 STEP 1
60 LET I = I+1
70 NEXT I
```

This would be repeated only 5 times. Be sure that the difference between this and rule (iii) is understood.

(vii) If the initial, final and step values are such that the loop should not be executed, it is jumped over. Thus the loop beginning with

```
66 FOR J = 1Ø TO 1 STEP 2
```

is not executed at all.

(viii) Loops can be jumped out of, that is, an IF . . . THEN or a GO TO within the loop could cause the program to leave the loop entirely.

(ix) Loops can be jumped into, but care must be taken that the loop variable has a suitable value. Jumping out and back in can be useful.

To match every FOR statement there must be a corresponding NEXT statement. The NEXT statement takes the form:

line number **NEXT** *variable*

which indicates the end of the loop. The named variable must obviously be the same one as in the corresponding FOR statement.*

3 Problems

Some of these problems are repetitions of those in Session 3. It will be found that the use of the FOR and NEXT statements is a great convenience.

PROBLEM 4.1   Write a program to evaluate the factorial of a number.

PROBLEM 4.2   Write a program to find out if a given number is prime.

PROBLEM 4.3   Write a program to evaluate $_nC_r$, the number of combinations of n objects taken r at a time:

$$_nC_r = \frac{n!}{r! \, (n - r)!}$$

4 Nesting FOR and NEXT loops

The solution of a problem often involves several loops contained within each other. For example it may be necessary to evaluate a function of two variables, I and J, over a range of values of each. Loops can be contained within each other in BASIC, but they cannot be allowed to overlap one

---

* Here BASIC indulges in a bit of redundancy for the benefit of program clarity. The language could have been designed with the variable name left out of the NEXT statement, and the implicit meaning would be the end of the most recent loop, which is always the case in BASIC. Even though it is redundant, the loop variable name must be given in the NEXT statement.

another, because if they do the intention of the program is ambiguous. The rule is that loops cannot cross: two examples serve to illustrate correct and incorrect use of double loops:

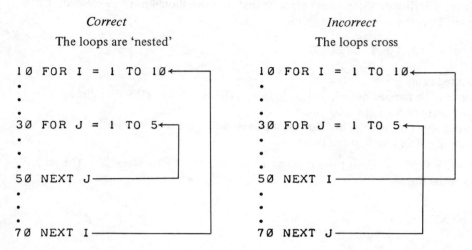

| *Correct* | *Incorrect* |
| The loops are 'nested' | The loops cross |

In the correct use of multiple loops, they must never cross one another, and so are said to be nested.

The other situation which cannot be allowed is the use of the same variable to count loops which are inside each other, as follows:

```
10 FOR I = 1 TO 10
 •
 •
 •
30 FOR I = 1 TO 5
 •
 •                                  not allowed
 •
50 NEXT I
 •
 •
 •

70 NEXT I
```

No sensible programmer would do this intentionally, but everyone is liable to violate this rule unintentionally, perhaps by leaving out the NEXT statement of a loop altogether.

Example The following program evaluates and prints the function of two variables

$$f(x, y) = \frac{1}{2\pi} e^{-(x+y)^2/2}$$

over the range $x = 0, 0.1, \ldots, 0.5$ and $y = 0, 0.1, \ldots, 0.5$ (which is the bivariate probability density function for a rather simplified case of the normal distribution)

```
1Ø  REM  EVALUATE  AND  PRINT  BIVARIATE  DISTRIBUTION
2Ø  LET  P  =  1/(2*ATN(1))
3Ø  FOR  Y  =  1  TO  Ø  STEP  -.2
4Ø  FOR  X  =  Ø  TO  1  STEP  .2
5Ø  LET  F  =  P*EXP(-(X↑2+Y↑2)/2)
6Ø  PRINT  F;
7Ø  NEXT  X
8Ø  PRINT
9Ø  NEXT  Y
1ØØ  END
```

There are two features of printing in this program which provide a taste of things to follow in the next session, where they will be explained.

5 Problems

PROBLEM 4.4   Find $_nC_r$ over the range $n = 0, 1, \ldots, 10$ and $r = 0, 1, \ldots n$. It may be worth copying the PRINT arrangements from the preceding example.

PROBLEM 4.5   Write a program to count the number of primes less than a given number.

6 Multiple Branching—the ON . . . GO TO statement

It is sometimes useful to be able to branch to one of several destinations in a program. The ON . . . GO TO statement allows a number of destinations to be given which depend on the outcome of an expression. The form of this is:

line number a **ON** *expression* **GO TO** *line number b*, *line number c*, . . . *etc.*

When this statement is encountered, the *expression* is evaluated and truncated to an integer value. Then if the result is 1, the program jumps to *line number b*, if 2 it jumps to *line number c*, if 3 to *d*, and so on. If the expression turns out to be either negative, zero, or too large for the number of destinations given, then an error has occurred and a suitable message will appear on the terminal.

As an example suppose a multiple choice examination is being given by computer, and the third option is the correct answer. The following program segment would suffice:

```
1Ø  PRINT"THE  STATEMENT  IN  BASIC  WHICH  ENDS  A  LOOP  IS:"
2Ø  PRINT"1  LET"
3Ø  PRINT"2  REPEAT"
4Ø  PRINT"3  NEXT"
5Ø  PRINT"4  REM"
6Ø  INPUT  I
7Ø  ON  I  GO  TO  8Ø,8Ø,1ØØ,8Ø
8Ø  PRINT"NO,  TRY  AGAIN"
9Ø  GO  TO  6Ø
1ØØ  PRINT"YES,  NOW  FOR  MY  NEXT  QUESTION  ....."
```

7 Problem

PROBLEM 4.6   Evaluate the roots of the quadratic equation $ax^2 + bx + c = 0$, covering the three types of discriminant with one ON . . . GO TO statement.

8 Summary Notes on Session 4

(a) The FOR statement:

line number **FOR** *variable* = *expression* **TO** *expression* **STEP** *expression*

> Begins a program loop.
> STEP is optional, and if not specified is taken as 1.
> The loop may be jumped over altogether. The initial, final and step values are fixed when the loop begins. The loop variable can be adjusted during the loop. With care a program can jump out of and into loops.
> There must be a corresponding NEXT statement.

(b) The NEXT statement:

line number **NEXT** *variable*

> Terminates a program loop. The named variable must be the same as the most recent unterminated loop variable.

(c) Loops using different variables can be nested but cannot overlap. Thus the NEXT statement must always correspond to the most recent unterminated loop.

(d) The ON . . . GO TO statement:

line number **ON** *expression* **GO TO** *line number a, line number b, . . . etc.*

> The *expression* is evaluated and truncated to an integer.
> If the result = 1, the program branches to *line number a*
> 2, the program branches to *line number b*
>   etc.
> Negative, zero, or too large a result causes an error condition.

9 Supplementary Problems

PROBLEM 4.7   The trapezoidal rule for numerical quadrature was introduced as problem 3.9, in
which

$$\int_{x_1}^{x_2} f(x)\,dx = \frac{f(x_1) + f(x_2)}{2(x_2 - x_1)}$$

for the curve shown in Fig. 4.2.

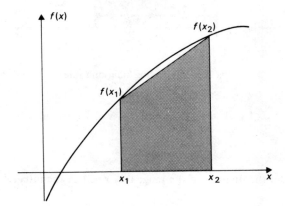

Fig. 4.2. Illustrating the trapezoidal rule.

As in the earlier problem, but this time using FOR and NEXT statements, find

$$\frac{1}{\sqrt{2\pi}} \int_0^1 e^{-x^2/2}\,dx$$

by dividing the range $0 \leqslant x \leqslant 1$ into ten equal segments and summing the areas of the
trapezoids so formed.

PROBLEM 4.8   A more accurate method than the trapezoidal rule is Simpson's rule in which
the area under the curve is found by fitting a parabolic segment to the curve and finding the
area under the parabola. Complicated as this may seem, it leads to the simple formula

$$\int_{x_1}^{x_3} f(x)\,dx = \frac{h}{6}\{f(x_1) + 4f(x_2) + f(x_3)\}$$

where $h = x_3 - x_2 = x_4 - x_3$ as shown in Fig. 4.3.

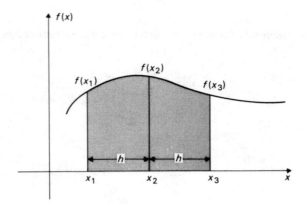

Fig. 4.3. Illustrating Simpson's rule.

Find $\dfrac{1}{\sqrt{2\pi}} \displaystyle\int_0^1 e^{-x^2/2}\ \mathrm{d}x$ by dividing the range $0 \leqslant x \leqslant 1$ into ten segments and using Simpson's rule

PROBLEM 4.9   Reconsider the division of the range $0 \leqslant x \leqslant 1$ in the integral

$$\frac{1}{\sqrt{2\pi}} \int_0^1 e^{-x^2/2}\ \mathrm{d}x$$

Divide the interval into only two segments and find the area by both Simpson's rule and the trapezoidal rule. Then repeat the evaluation doubling the number of segments until both methods give better than 4 figures accuracy. How much better is Simpson's rule? In selecting a stopping criterion, it may be wise to consider the theoretical variation of the errors in these methods as the step size h is varied. For the trapezoidal rule, the errors vary with h^2, while using Simpson's rule they are proportional to h^4. As with the Newton-Raphson iteration in Session 2, the improvement in the next stage can be predicted roughly and so an unnecessary stage can be saved.

PROBLEM 4.10   The term 'numerical integration' also applies to the solution of differential equations by numerical means. A wide variety of methods are available, but one of the most popular is a class of techniques known collectively as the Runge-Kutta methods. Given an equation

$$\frac{\mathrm{d}y}{\mathrm{d}t} = f(y,\ t)$$

for which y_0 is known at t_0, and $y\,(t_0 + h)$ is desired. This requirement can be met by calculating, in order, the following quantities:

$$k_0 = hf(y_0, t_0)$$
$$k_1 = hf(y_0 + k_0/2, t_0 + h/2)$$
$$k_2 = hf(y_0 + k_1/2, t_0 + h/2)$$
$$k_3 = hf(y_0 + k_2, t_0 + h)$$

after which the value for $y(t + h)$ is found as:

$$y(t + h) = \tfrac{1}{6}(k_0 + 2k_1 + 2k_2 + k_3)$$

This is then a Runge–Kutta procedure of fourth order. Use this method to solve the equation

$$\frac{dy}{dt} = -y$$

with $y = 1$ at $t = 0$. Begin with $h = 0.1$ and carry out the solution for $t = 0, h, 2h, \ldots,$ 4 seconds. Then try $h = 0.2, 0.4, \ldots$.

PROBLEM 4.11   The Runge–Kutta procedure can be used for higher order equations by breaking them down to a series of first order equations and applying the method simultaneously to the whole set. Thus the equation

$$\frac{d^2 y}{dt^2} = -y$$

can be broken down into two equations

$$\frac{dy_1}{dt} = y_2$$

and

$$\frac{dy_2}{dt} = -y_1$$

To obtain the solution, the quantity k_0 is first found for both equations (giving a value for each), then k_1 and so on.
Solve the equations

(i) $\dfrac{d^2 y}{dt^2} = -y$ with $y(0) = 0$ and $\dfrac{dy(0)}{dt} = 1$

(ii) $\dfrac{d^2 y}{dt^2} = t\left(\dfrac{dy}{dt}\right)^2 - y^2$ with $y(0) = 0$ and $\dfrac{dy(0)}{dt} = 0$

PROBLEM 4.12   It is possible to find the value of π by repeatedly dropping a needle onto a piece of paper with two parallel lines ruled upon it. Suppose, as in Fig. 4.4 the lines are one unit apart and the needle is one unit long. Assume the needle falls so that at least one end is between the lines, and that all distances y from the lower line and all angles ϕ that the needle makes with the lines are equally probable, then the probability that the needle crosses one of the lines is $2/\pi$.

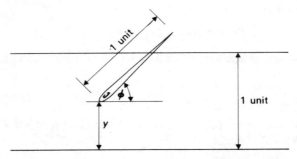

Fig. 4.4. Position of the needle falling between parallel lines in the determination of π by the method of statistical trials.

The RND function can be used to find the value of π by numerically tossing the needle a large number of times, selecting random values of y between 0 and 1 and ϕ between 0 and 2π radians. If the total number of tosses is recorded along with the total number of crossings, then their ratio can be used to find π. This is one of the simplest examples of the method of statistical trials or 'Monte Carlo' method which can be used to solve a wide variety of equations, including partial differential equations.

Find π in this way. How many trials are needed to give two significant digits. Four? Six? (if the computer time can be afforded).

SESSION 5
PRINTER ZONING AND GRAPH PLOTTING

1 Introduction

The PRINT statement of BASIC provides certain limited ways of controlling the alignment and spacing of printed output on the terminal. The use of PRINT in typing captions and numerical output has been demonstrated. In simple BASIC it is also possible to control the placement and spacing of numerical output, but only to a certain extent. It often will be found that a desired output format cannot be achieved or that certain kinds of tabulation are not possible; it is in PRINT zoning that the first serious limitations of elementary BASIC will appear. BASIC is intentionally a rather simple language, and so only certain types of zoning are available with the ordinary PRINT statement.*

However, in another sense, BASIC is more versatile than some other languages in the facilities which allow graphs to be plotted and lines of output to be continued from one PRINT statement to the next.

When the PRINT statement was introduced in Session 1, no attempt was made to describe the extent of available control over the spacing of printed output. This Session treats the PRINT statement in some detail, and introduces the graph plotting ability of BASIC.

2 Printer Zoning—the comma as delimiter

BASIC provides three means of controlling the alignment of printed information: the comma and semicolon as delimiters, and a special function, the TAB function. The general form of the PRINT statement will now be stated:

line number **PRINT** *quantity delimiter quantity delimiter* . . .

where *quantity* can represent either expressions of any complexity, character strings, or the special TAB function.

delimiter can be a comma or a semicolon, and can sometimes be omitted.

Example

```
75 PRINT A,B+C,TAB(D);"CHARACTER STRING"
```

Quantities: A
      B+C
      TAB(D)
      "CHARACTER STRING"

---

* Some extensions to BASIC have a PRINT USING statement which does allow powerful output control, but introduces additional syntax requirements to the print control feature. Details of this are given in Session 11, but it is not widely available at the time of writing.

Delimiters: , (comma)
      ; (semicolon)

The printing of numerical output separated by commas will be considered first. The exact form of representation of a number is not controllable in the simple PRINT statement, and the choice made by BASIC depends on the nature and size of the number. It may be printed as an integer, or with decimal places, or in the exponential format. Whenever the quantities to be printed are separated by commas, BASIC divides the line of print into 5 zones of 15 spaces each. Printing always begins at the beginning of the first zone. A comma causes printing of the next number to start at the beginning of the next zone, i.e. in the 16th space. Regardless of the form each individual number takes, they are always printed in the same five positions across the page. Therefore tables can be printed which contain five or fewer columns, and although the form chosen by BASIC may vary the columns will always be aligned.

EXERCISE Investigate the printing of integers on the terminal. Find out how large they can be before they are printed in exponential format.

EXERCISE Investigate the printing of nonintegers on the terminal. Find out how large they can be before they are printed in exponential format.

EXERCISE Find out what happens if more than five quantities are printed separated by commas.

3 Printer Zoning—the semicolon as delimiter

If a semicolon is used in place of the comma in PRINT statements, then the printed output is squeezed together. The result is that more numbers can be printed on a line. Unfortunately the field size when the semicolon is used may vary according to the number of digits in the result. Thus tabulation of results varies with their nature and magnitude.

EXERCISE Find out how many numbers of a given size or type can be squeezed into a line using a semicolon. This information will be needed in problem 5.1.

A common use of the semicolon is in continuing printed output on the same line with several PRINT statements. If a semicolon is given as delimiter after the last quantity in a PRINT statement, then the next PRINT statement continues on the same line.

EXERCISE Run the following example:

```
1 Ø  FOR  I  =  1  TO  1 Ø
2 Ø  PRINT  I;
3 Ø  NEXT  I
4 Ø  END
```

A PRINT statement with no quantities or delimiters at all, i.e. with no output, causes the next PRINT statement to start on a new line.

EXERCISE   Run the example

```
10 FOR I = 1 TO 5
20 FOR J = 1 TO 5
30 PRINT J;
40 NEXT J
50 PRINT
60 NEXT I
70 END
```

4 Printer Zoning–The TAB function

The semicolon may seem a weak facility, but in conjunction with the TAB function it provides many useful features including a measure of control over printer zoning and graph plotting.

TAB is a special function which can be used only in PRINT statements. It appears with a single argument such as TAB (X), where X can be an expression of any complexity. It causes the printer to move along the print line to the column given by the integer part of X, which obviously should be an existing column number. Thus X cannot be negative or too large. TAB (X) is normally followed by a semicolon so that printing will start in the next column, i.e. column $INT(X)+1$. If TAB (X) is followed by a comma, then the printer will move to the beginning of the next of its usual 15 column fields; this is usually undesirable.

EXERCISE   Try the following example:

```
10 FOR I = 1 TO 10
20 PRINT TAB(I);I
30 NEXT I
40 END
```

It is important to note that the TAB function cannot move the printer backwards, and if this is attempted it will have no effect. To move to column 60 from column 50, TAB (60) is used (not TAB (10).

5 Problem–printing Pascal's triangle

Pascal's triangle is the arrangement of the coefficients of binomial expansions in triangular form, as in Fig. 5.1,

$$_0C_0$$

$$_1C_0 \qquad _1C_1$$

$$_2C_0 \qquad _2C_1 \qquad _2C_2$$

$$_3C_0 \qquad _3C_1 \qquad _3C_2 \qquad _3C_3$$

$$_4C_0 \qquad _4C_1 \qquad _4C_2 \qquad _4C_3 \qquad _4C_4$$

Fig. 5.1. Pascal's triangle.

so that the first five lines are:

PROBLEM 5.1   Write a program to print the first 10 lines of Pascal's triangle. The calculation of $_nC_r$ was given as problems 3.1 and 4.1. The spacing of integers was determined in the previous exercise, and the zoning can be controlled by the TAB function so that the printed numbers line up properly.

6 Printer Zoning—graph plotting

Character strings can be treated like any other quantity in print zoning. Therefore the TAB function can be used to move the printer to a desired column where a character string can then begin. This provides the means of plotting graphs on the printer. Note that the printer column specified must lie within the number of printer spaces available; this usually requires some scaling of a graph. The following exercises show examples of a line graph and a bar graph.

EXERCISE   Run the program:

```
10 FOR I = 1 TO 10
20 PRINT TAB(I);"X"
30 NEXT I
40 END
```

EXERCISE   Run the same example but change line 20 to read:

```
20 PRINT TAB(I);"X";
```

EXERCISE   Run the following program:

```
10 FOR I = 1 TO 10
20 FOR J = 1 TO I
30 PRINT TAB(30+J);"X";
40 NEXT J
50 PRINT
60 NEXT I
70 END
```

Character strings have one special feature in print zoning, which is that the delimiter can be omitted before or after the string. If this is done a semicolon is assumed except at the end of a line, where printing continued on the same line must be specified explicitly by a semicolon.

EXERCISE   Run the previous three examples again, omitting the redundant semicolons.

7 Problems

PROBLEM 5.2   Plot a full cycle of a cosine wave on the terminal of amplitude 25 print positions and period 20 lines.

Solution

```
10 LET T = 8*ATN(1)/20
20 FOR I = 0 TO 19
30 PRINT TAB(25.5+25*COS(T*I));"*"
40 NEXT I
50 END
```

Notes (i)   The calculation $T = 8*ATN(1)/20$ is taken outside the loop for efficiency.

(ii)   The TAB function includes 'rounding' by the addition of 0.5 to make the function smoother.

PROBLEM 5.3   To a suitable scale plot the polynomial $f(x) = x^3 - 7.8\,x^2 + 18.5\,x - 11.3$ for $0 \leqslant x \leqslant 4$.

PROBLEM 5.4   To a suitable scale, plot the polynomial $f(x) = x^3 - 7.8\,x^2 + 18.5\,x - 11.3$ with the X–axis shown.

PROBLEM 5.5   Plot a full cycle of a sine wave and a cosine wave together on the terminal.

PROBLEM 5.6   Plot a full cycle of a cosine wave as a shaded graph, i.e. as a bar graph drawn from the zero level of the waveform.

8 Summary Notes on Session 5

(a) The PRINT statement

line number **PRINT** *quantity delimiter quantity delimiter* . . .

The requested information is printed on the terminal.
quantity = an expression which results in numerical output,
a character string resulting in literal output,
or the TAB function.
delimiter = a comma or semicolon, may be omitted before or after strings, is optional at the
end of the print statement.
A PRINT statement starts a new line unless a final delimiter was explicitly given in the previous
PRINT.
A PRINT statement containing too many quantities for a single line will be continued on the
following line.

(b) The comma:
The print line is divided into 5 zones of 15 spaces.
The comma causes the next quantity to be printed beginning in the first space of the next
zone.

(c) The semicolon:
between quantities causes the output to be compressed.
After a TAB function or a character string printing continues in the next space. Between
numerical output the spacing depends on the numbers (see (d)), for example with small
integers it is 6 spaces.
At the end of a print statement the semicolon causes the next print statement to continue
on the same line.

(d) Numbers:
can appear as integers, or as numbers with decimal places, or in exponential format.

(e) Character strings:
The quotation marks surrounding character strings enable the delimiter to be left out, in
which case a semicolon is assumed except at the end of a PRINT statement, where the
absence of a delimiter causes the next PRINT statement to start a new line.

(f) The TAB function:
TAB (expression) may appear as a quantity in a PRINT statement. This causes the printer
to move forward to the line number given by the integer part of the expression. Obviously
the expression must specify a column number which exists, and the printer cannot be moved
backwards.

9 Supplementary Problems

PROBLEM 5.7   Calculate and plot the density of occurrence of prime numbers in the ranges
0–1000, 1000–2000, etc.

PROBLEM 5.8   Calculate and plot the solution of the ordinary differential equation

$$\frac{d^2 y}{dt^2} = -y$$

for which $y(0) = 1$ and $dy(0)/dt = 0$ using the Runge-Kutta method (Problems 4.10 and 4.11).

PROBLEM 5.9   Stirling's approximation to the factorial of large numbers is

$$n! \approx \sqrt{2\pi}\, n \left(\frac{n}{e}\right)^n$$

Were this formula reasonably accurate, then a plot of $n!$ against the corresponding Stirling
approximation would be the line of form Y = X.
Calculate and plot a graph which shows the accuracy of this approximation.

PROBLEM 5.10   Calculate and plot simultaneously the function

$$\frac{1}{\sqrt{2\pi}}\, e^{-x^2/2}$$

and the integral

$$0.5 + \frac{1}{\sqrt{2\pi}} \int\limits_{0}^{x} e^{-x^2/2}\, dx$$

found by either the trapezoidal rule or Simpson's rule, as defined in problems 4.7 and 4.8.

SESSION 6
FUNCTIONS AND SUBROUTINES

1 Introduction

This session describes how a programmer can define his own functions and subroutines to simplify a BASIC program. The standard functions of BASIC have already been used in many of the problems, and they cover the most important requirements. In addition to these it is possible to define new functions, but in a restricted way. Functions can, however, greatly shorten a program by replacing arithmetic expressions which occur frequently.

Subroutines are even more useful than functions. In earlier sessions, repeated calculations have often been simplified by using FOR and NEXT statements. However, it is sometimes not possible to include every repetition of a given sequence of calculations in a loop, and a subroutine provides a means of using the same calculation at places scattered throughout the program. The use of subroutines can also make complicated programs easier to understand by breaking them down into straightforward modules, although if this is carried to extremes the resulting program can be more difficult to understand.

It will be seen that many earlier problems can be simplified using subroutines, and the problems of this session are concerned largely with rewriting earlier programs.

2 Defining Functions—the DEF FN statement

A function is defined by the DEF FN statement, whose form is:

line number **DEF FN***a* (*variable*) = *expression*

In one program, 26 functions are available, for the keyword FN*a* can be FNA, FNB, . . . , FNZ. The same function name FN*a* should not be defined more than once in the program; on most computers this would not be allowed. '

The variable in brackets is called the 'argument' of the function, and will normally appear in the expression on the right hand side, but need not. Whenever the function is encountered in a running program, the expression on the right hand side is evaluated with the value of the given argument substituted for the variable in the function definition.

For example, the statement:

```
99 DEF FNC(R) = 4*ATN(1)*R↑2
```

calculates the area of a circle given its radius as argument. If the following statement appears in the same BASIC program:

```
88 LET X = FNC(A)+FNC(10)
```

the function will provide the area of a circle of radius 10 and the area of a circle of radius A; these are added together to become the new value of variable X. Even if R is given a value in the program, it is *not* used by the function unless, of course, a BASIC statement calls for FNC(R). The argument used in the function is what is called a 'dummy argument'.

A new function can be defined anywhere in a BASIC program, not necessarily before the line that first uses it. Unfortunately the definition of a function is limited to an expression of one line, and it can only have a single argument.* If variables other than the function argument appear in the expression, then their actual values are used in the calculation, i.e. they are not dummies. Functions can use other functions, but obviously a function cannot use itself, nor can an endless loop of functions be permitted.

3 Problems

PROBLEM 6.1   Use a function to provide

$$\frac{1}{\sqrt{2\pi}} e^{-x^2/2}$$

and plot a graph of this between $x = 0$ and $x = 4$.

PROBLEM 6.2   Use a function to find the remainder after division of positive integers. Make the numerator the function argument.

PROBLEM 6.3   The INT function is not a true truncation, as INT(−3.6) gives −4, whereas a truncation would give −3. Provide a function which truncates its argument.

PROBLEM 6.4   Provide a function for rounded truncation, i.e. $f(3.4) = 3$ but $f(3.6) = 4$.

4 Defining Subroutines—The GOSUB and RETURN statements

A subroutine is a separate program module not restricted to one line. The program calls for the subroutine explicitly by jumping to its first line, in contrast to the implicit way functions are used. A subroutine can be written as a self-contained unit, starting at any line number which does not occur elsewhere, and containing only unique line numbers in sequence. The usual practice is to begin with a large line number, often in the thousands. The subroutine is terminated by a RETURN statement, and to jump to a subroutine in a BASIC program, the GOSUB statement is included. This can be best illustrated by an example. Suppose that N9 is a positive integer, or zero, and that its factorial is required. A BASIC subroutine could be provided

---

* Some forms of BASIC do provide in addition a multiple line function definition, and this is described in Session 11.

to find factorial N9, as N8. The following example illustrates the definition and use of a subroutine to calculate factorials with a suggested layout for flowcharts with subroutines. Referring first to the flow diagram of Fig. 6.1 it is seen that the 'main program' and subroutine have separate flowcharts.

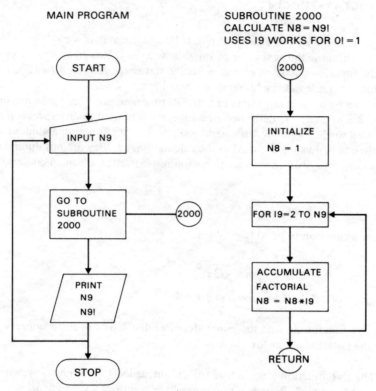

Fig. 6.1. Flow diagrams showing the layout of a subroutine.

The flow diagram translates easily into the BASIC program:

```
10 REM THIS IS A PROGRAM TO FIND FACTORIALS
20 REM OF NUMBERS TYPED IN TO THE TERMINAL
30 REM
40 REM REQUEST INPUT
50 PRINT"NUMBER WHOSE FACTORIAL IS REQUIRED";
60 INPUT N9
70 GOSUB 2000
80 PRINT"FACTORIAL "N9"IS "N8
90 GO TO 50
2000 REM SUBROUTINE TO FIND FACTORIAL OF N9
2010 REM THE ANSWER IS RETURNED IN N8
2020 REM VARIABLE I9 IS USED
```

```
2030 LET N8 = 1
2040 FOR I9 = 2 TO N9
2050 LET N8 = N8*I9
2060 NEXT I9
2070 RETURN
2080 END
```

Several things should be noted here:

(i) The subroutine is called from the main program by the GOSUB statement.

(ii) It is returned to the main program by the RETURN statement.

(iii) The subroutine always finds the factorial of N9, and gives the answer as N8. Variable I9 is also used by the subroutine. This means that the same variables are shared by all parts of a BASIC program. Complicated subroutines will probably use many BASIC variables, and care must be taken not to destroy any variables that are necessary to other parts of the program. This lack of isolation between main program and subroutine is one of the disadvantages of BASIC.*

(iv) The END statement is still required to be the highest numbered statement of the entire program.

EXERCISE   Run this program. Note the effect of the semicolon in line 50.

The statements provided for subroutine usage are:

line number a **GOSUB** *line number b*

When this statement is encountered, execution of the BASIC program continues from *line number b* until a RETURN statement is encountered, when the program returns to the line after *line number a*.

line number **RETURN**

This statement causes a return from a subroutine to the place where the call occurred. (This place could be in another subroutine.)

The power of the subroutine lies in its ability to return from whence it came. Thus one subroutine could call another and so on. However, it is obvious that neither should one subroutine call itself, nor should an endless loop of several subroutines be established.

5 Terminating Program Execution—the STOP statement

Before subroutines were introduced, the END statement was sufficient to terminate a program. The END statement is required to be the highest numbered line in the BASIC program, subroutines and all. It could still be used for termination, by jumping to it. However the STOP

---

* Subroutines in elementary BASIC do not provide the advantages of dummy arguments. Session 11 describes how these can be used in some extensions to BASIC.

statement is provided for termination and can have any line number and so take any position in the program. It is simply:

line number **STOP**

and when it is encountered, execution of the program stops.

Thus, in the example of section 4, line 90 could have been a STOP statement, but not an END statement.

6 Problems

PROBLEM 6.5   Using a subroutine to find factorials, write a main program to evaluate $_nC_r$ given n and r.

PROBLEM 6.6   Transform the calculation of $_nC_r$ into a subroutine which itself calls the factorial subroutine.

PROBLEM 6.7   Evaluate and print Pascal's triangle using subroutines (see problem 5.1).

PROBLEM 6.8   Write a subroutine for bar graph plotting and use it to plot a cosine wave.

PROBLEM 6.9   Define functions to evaluate hyperbolic sine and cosine.

$$\sinh x = \frac{e^x - e^{-x}}{2} \qquad \cosh x = \frac{e^x + e^{-x}}{2}$$

and plot them over the range $-2 \leqslant x \leqslant 2$ using the bar graph plotting subroutines.

PROBLEM 6.10   Using the functions of problem 6.9, make another function to evaluate

$$\tanh x = \frac{\sinh x}{\cosh x}$$

and plot it over the range $-2 \leqslant x \leqslant 2$.

7 Summary Notes on Session 6

(a) Functions are defined by the DEF FN statement:

line number **DEF FN***a* (*variable*) = *expression*

> *a* can be the letters A through Z, thus the 26 names FNA, FNB, . . . FNZ are available.
> When the function name is implicitly used in a running program, the expression on the right
> hand side is evaluated using the given value of the function variable. The function variable is
> thus a 'dummy' for the value used while running.
> Only one definition of a particular function should be used.
> Functions may use other functions, but endless loops may not be so established.

(b) Subroutines are called by the GOSUB statement:

line number a **GOSUB** *line number b*

> The running program continues from *line number b* until a RETURN is encountered, when it
> carries on from the line after *line number a*. Subroutines may call other subroutines, but endless
> loops may not be so established.

(c) Subroutines are ended by the RETURN statement:

line number **RETURN**

> The running program returns to the line after the latest GOSUB.

(d) The STOP statement terminates program execution:

line number **STOP**

8 Supplementary Problems

PROBLEM 6.11   Write a subroutine which finds the area of a trapezoidal element, given X8 and X9 as the bounds and calling a function for the function values as in Fig. 6.2.

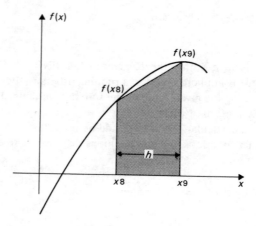

Fig. 6.2. Illustrating the trapezoidal rule.

$$\text{Area} = \frac{h}{2}\,(f(X8) + f(X9))$$

Using this find the integrals:

(i) $\dfrac{1}{\sqrt{2\pi}} \displaystyle\int_0^1 e^{-x^2/2}\,\mathrm{d}x$

(ii) $\displaystyle\int_0^{\pi/2} \dfrac{\mathrm{d}x}{\sqrt{1 - \dfrac{\sin^2 x}{4}}}$

(iii) $\displaystyle\int_0^{\pi/2} \sqrt{1 - \dfrac{\sin^2 x}{4}}$

PROBLEM 6.12   Repeat problem 6.11 using a subroutine which evaluates the area enclosed by X7, X8, and X9 by Simpson's rule as shown in Fig. 6.3.

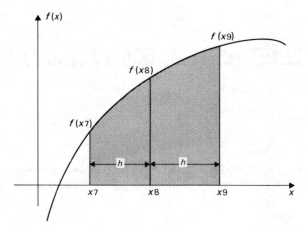

Fig. 6.3.

$$\text{Area} = \frac{h}{6}\left(f(X7) + 4f(X8) + f(X9)\right)$$

PROBLEM 6.13   Using a subroutine for the Runge–Kutta integration (problem 4.10), solve the ordinary differential equation

$$\frac{d^2y}{dt^2} + 2\frac{dy}{dt} + 5y = 1$$

with $y(0) = 0$ and $dy(0)/dt = 0$

and plot the result using a subroutine which prints both the zero level and the present value of a function.

PROBLEM 6.14   Write a subroutine to find the roots of the equation $x^5 - x = 9$ using

 (i) The Newton–Raphson iteration (Session 2)
 (ii) The method of false position (Problem 2.11)

These programs should call for defined functions to provide the function value and derivative when required.

SESSION 7
ARRAYS AND SUBSCRIPTS IN ONE DIMENSION

1 Introduction

Any program which attempts to deal with a list of values having the same meaning, but using separate variable names, presents difficulties to the programmer. First of all, the program steps would have to be written out separately for each member of the list. Additionally, the required number of variables in many practical situations could become so large that all 286 available variable names were exhausted.

Most computing languages provide what is called an array facility: a means of organizing a list of values under only one variable name. The particular member or element of the array desired in a program can be accessed by the use of subscripts, and a common calculation can be applied to the entire array by varying the subscript, for example by using a FOR . . . NEXT loop.

Arrays and subscripts, then, are a great convenience in the organization of programs which must deal with a number of values all having the same meaning. These features of BASIC are of sufficient importance that three sessions are devoted to their description. In this session the concepts of arrays and subscripts are introduced and applied to the case of one dimension.

2 Arrays and Subscripts

In BASIC an ordered set of quantities can be given one variable name, and treated as an array. A particular member of the array can be selected by the use of a subscript. A variable is automatically treated as an array if it is used with a subscript, and the subscript itself can be any expression in BASIC. A subscripted variable is written as the variable name with the subscript in parentheses.

Example
A(3)   refers to the third member of array A
B(I+J) refers to the (I+J)th member of array B

Although a subscript can be any expression, it is obvious that it has to be interpreted as a positive integer. In BASIC, the lower limit of subscripts is 1.* If the subscript is not an integer, it is truncated to an integer, thus:

C(3.75) refers to the 3rd element of C.

BASIC keeps a running check on the validity of subscripts so if subscripts occur which are less than one, or too large, then the running program will be terminated. The same variable name should

---

* This is the usual practice. Subscript 0 is allowed on some systems, as is recommended in the Specification for Standard Basic referred to in the Preface.

not be used in both subscripted and unsubscripted form. Unsubscripted variables of the kind that have been used up to this point are properly called scalar variables.

It is easy to confuse the subscript, which refers to a certain member of the array, with the value which that member contains.

Example   Everyone knows that prisoners are dehumanized by being assigned numbers, which are prominently displayed on their clothing. Suppose a prison has 4 cells, each occupied by one prisoner. Then the set of prisoner numbers could form an array of length 4, and the subscripts could correspond to the numbering of the cells, as Fig. 7.1.

CELL No.1   CELL No.2   CELL No.3   CELL No.4

 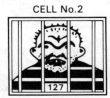  

Fig. 7.1. An array of prisoners.

The contents of this array could be described as:

	Subscript	Value
The prisoner in cell	1	is 631
The prisoner in cell	2	is 127
The prisoner in cell	3	is 458
The prisoner in cell	4	is 390

In a BASIC program, the array of prison numbers could be called N. Subscripts 1 to 4 specify different cells, and the prisoner numbers are N(1), N(2), N(3) and N(4). Once defined these prison numbers can be used in calculations.

EXERCISE   Try the following simple program which reads in the prisoner numbers one at a time, and prints them out again.

```
10 PRINT"TYPE IN THE PRISONER NUMBERS ONE AT A TIME"
20 FOR I = 1 TO 4
30 INPUT N(I)
40 NEXT I
50 FOR J = 4 TO 1 STEP -1
60 PRINT"THE PRISONER IN CELL"J"IS NUMBER"N(J)
70 NEXT J
80 END
```

Additional arrays could be defined to tell us more about the prisoners. The length of unexpired sentence might be one item of interest, and as long as the correspondence between arrays is preserved, then this could be defined as a new array called L, for example:

Cell:	1	2	3	4
Prisoner Number:	631	127	458	390
Unexpired Sentence:	99	1	53	30

3 Problems

Use these problems to experiment with arrays and subscripts, but do not attempt to use subscripts greater than 10.

PROBLEM 7.1   Write a program to find and print the cell number and prisoner number cf the prisoner with:

   (i) The highest prisoner number. This can be found by setting aside a variable H for the highest prisoner number and comparing it with each prisoner number in turn. Whenever a higher number than H is found, it should replace H.
  (ii) The lowest prisoner number.
 (iii) The prisoner number nearest the mean.

Define the array of prisoner numbers by having them typed in, as in the example.

PROBLEM 7.2   Write a program to determine and print the cell number of the prisoner with:

   (i) The longest unexpired sentence.
  (ii) The shortest unexpired sentence.
 (iii) The unexpired sentence nearest the mean.

4 Defining Longer Arrays—the DIM statement

The space requirements of an array have not been of concern in the previous problems because BASIC assumes that any array of one dimension has 10 members. No difficulty arises if fewer than 10 are actually used as in the previous example. However BASIC provides a means for explicitly stating the size of an array so that longer arrays can be used. It is also good practice not to use more space than necessary, and occasionally even a small saving in computer resources can be valuable. Therefore array lengths shorter than 10 can also be stated explicitly.

   The length of arrays is stated explicitly by the DIM statement, where DIM is short for DIMENSION:

$$line\ number\ \textbf{DIM}\ \begin{matrix} array\ variable \\ name\ a \end{matrix} \begin{pmatrix} integer \\ number \end{pmatrix},\ \begin{matrix} array\ variable \\ name\ b \end{matrix} \begin{pmatrix} integer \\ number \end{pmatrix}\ \cdots$$

The integer number specifies the size of the named array. The DIM statement can appear anywhere in the program. A given variable name should only appear in one DIM statement.

Examples

```
5 DIM N(4),L(4)
```

reserves 4 spaces for each of arrays N and L. This statement could have been used in the previous exercises.

```
63 DIM X7(200)
```

reserves 200 spaces for variable X7.

5 Problems

PROBLEM 7.3   Write a program to convert a decimal number in the range ±32767 to any base from 2 to 9, using successive division by the base.

With successive division, the digits of the result are found in reverse order. Using an array these can be saved by working backwards through the array, so producing the final result in correct order. Alternatively, the array of results could be printed in reverse order.

First work out on paper the answer which will need the longest array to find out how large an array is required.

Example   Find 131 to base 7
Successive division by 7:

$$131/7 = 18 + 5/7; \qquad \text{Remainder} = 5$$
$$18/7 = 2 + 4/7; \qquad \text{Remainder} = 4$$
$$2/7 = 0 + 2/7; \qquad \text{Remainder} = 2$$

The answer to base 7 is 245 i.e. the remainders taken in reverse order.

6 Shuffling Arrays

In calculations using scalar variable names, the idea of replacing one variable by a new value after calculation has occurred frequently, for example in the recurrence relationship of a series evaluation. The same concept also applies to array calculations, except that the replacements are often done in some ordered way within the array. As an illustration the same prisoners could be required to rotate their cells, so that each moves down one cell number, except the prisoner in cell 1, who moves to cell 4.

In a computer program only one value can be moved at a time; in the prison analogy this would correspond to having only one guard to move the prisoners. The sequence of operations would be:

The prisoner in cell 1 moves out temporarily
The old prisoner in cell 2 becomes the new prisoner in cell 1.
The old prisoner in cell 3 becomes the new prisoner in cell 2.
The old prisoner in cell 4 becomes the new prisoner in cell 3.
and finally
The old prisoner in cell 1 becomes the new prisoner in cell 4.

It is noted that temporary storage of the old prisoner in cell 1 is required if he is not to escape. This can be shown diagrammatically, as in Fig. 7.2.

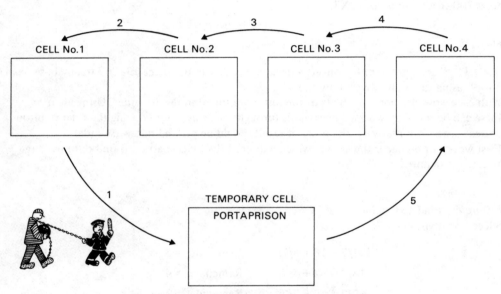

Fig. 7.2. Rotating the prisoners down one cell.

The effect of this reshuffling is:

	Before			After	
	Cell	Prisoner		Cell	Prisoner
	1	631		1	127
	2	127		2	458
	3	458		3	390
	4	390		4	631

If there are other arrays associated with the original order, then these should also be shuffled.

The prisoners moving into cells 1 and 3 would not be happy if they inherited the previous inmate's sentence.

A program segment which moves the prisoners and keeps track of their sentences could be:

```
30 REM STORE PRISONER FROM CELL 1 TEMPORARILY
40 LET X1 = N(1)
50 LET X2 = L(1)
60 REM MOVE THE OTHERS DOWN ONE CELL
70 FOR I = 1 TO 3
80 LET N(I) = N(I+1)
90 LET L(I) = L(I+1)
100 NEXT I
110 REM PUT TEMPORARY PRISONER IN CELL 4
120 LET N(4) = X1
130 LET L(4) = X2
```

A very common and embarrassing program error arises if the shuffle is done in the wrong sequence. The prisoners have been moved down in ascending cell order. If they had been moved down in descending order, then the old prisoner in cell 4 would be in cells 1, 2, and 3 and it would be some time before the other two were missed. Thus the shuffle can be performed downwards in ascending order, in which case the first convict goes into temporary storage. Alternatively they can be moved upwards in descending order in which case the temporary storage is used for the last convict. Naturally enough, if the release date of the man in temporary storage has arrived, then the temporary cell is not necessary. Therefore, the temporary storage is only used when the appropriate end value of an array must be preserved.

7 Problem

PROBLEM 7.4   Write programs to arrange the prisoners in

(i) ascending order of prisoner number and
(ii) descending order of sentence.

This kind of operation, called bubble sorting, involves a lot of shuffling.

As the material of this section is fundamental to what follows, it is recommended that at least some of the supplementary problems should be tried.

8 Summary Notes on Session 7

(a) An array is an ordered set of variables given one name. The use of a variable in a subscripted sense implies that it is an array,* for example in one dimension:

$$\text{array name} \longrightarrow$$
$$A (I + 3 * J)$$
$$\longmapsto \text{subscript}$$

(b) An array element is selected by the subscript which appears in parentheses after the array name. A subscript can be any expression, but the result should be between 1 and the maximum array size. If not an integer it is truncated to one, i.e.

$$A(3.73) \text{ means } A(3)$$

(c) The same variable name should not be used as an array and an ordinary (scalar) variable.
(d) A subscripted variable can be used in any BASIC statement which allows variables.
(e) An array of one dimension is assumed to be of length 10 unless otherwise stated by a DIM statement.
(f) The DIM (for DIMENSION) statement has the form:

$$\textit{line number } \textbf{DIM} \begin{smallmatrix} \textit{array variable} \\ \textit{name a} \end{smallmatrix} \begin{pmatrix} \textit{integer} \\ \textit{number} \end{pmatrix} , \begin{smallmatrix} \textit{array variable} \\ \textit{name b} \end{smallmatrix} \begin{pmatrix} \textit{integer} \\ \textit{number} \end{pmatrix} \cdots$$

---

* This is why the multiplication operation '*' must be explicitly included in arithmetic expressions. An expression $A(I+3*J)$ is taken as being subscripted, and does not mean the same as $A*(I+3*J)$.

9 Supplementary Problems

PROBLEM 7.5   In the Pascal triangle (Problem 5.1) note that each number is the sum of the two above it. Therefore each row can be generated from the previous one. Write a program to evaluate and print Pascal's triangle one row at a time without using $_nC_r$.

PROBLEM 7.6   Write a program to estimate the mean and variance of a series of numbers. The mean μ of a series of n numbers x_i is

$$\mu = \frac{1}{n} \sum_{i=1}^{n} x_i \quad \text{and the variance is } \sigma^2 = \frac{1}{n-1} \sum_{i=1}^{n} (x_i - \mu)^2$$

PROBLEM 7.7   The average of a fixed number of successive random numbers should itself be a random number with approximately normal distribution about the mean 0.5. If 12 numbers from RND are used the standard deviation should be 1. Using a subroutine to provide the random numbers, with supposedly normal distribution, find the mean and variance of 10, 100, and 1000 such numbers.

PROBLEM 7.8   Form a histogram of the distribution of the random numbers produced by the method described in Problem 7.7.
Do this by dividing the range 0–1 into 25 intervals, and count the total number of random numbers that fall into each part of the range from 1000 generated. Plot this histogram as a bar graph.

PROBLEM 7.9   Poisson distributed random numbers can also be generated. Suppose numbers are desired with mean e^{-m}. Using RND find a random number X_1. If $X_1 \leqslant e^{-m}$ then the new Poisson number is 1.
If not, find a new random number X_2, and if $X_1 X_2 \leqslant e^{-m}$, the new Poisson number is 2, and so on.
Thus in general k numbers are generated by the RND function until $X_1 X_2 \ldots X_k \leqslant e^{-m}$ and then k is the next Poisson number.
Using a subroutine to find the Poisson distributed numbers, form a histogram of the distribution of 1000 such numbers, and plot it.

PROBLEM 7.10   The distribution of temperature in a thin bar, Fig. 7.3, obeys the partial differential equation

$$\frac{\partial^2 T}{\partial x^2} = k \frac{\partial T}{\partial t}$$

In the steady-state situation, this would be $\dfrac{\partial^2 T}{\partial x^2} = 0$

To solve this equation numerically, it is usual to construct an equation which models the partial differential equation over discrete intervals.

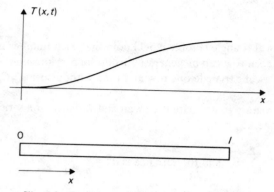

Fig. 7.3. Temperature distribution in a thin rod.

Supposing the bar is being considered over three pieces near the centre, as in Fig. 7.4. Then two estimates of $\partial T/\partial x$ in this region would be

$$\frac{\partial T}{\partial x} \simeq \frac{T_k - T_{k-1}}{h} \qquad \text{and} \qquad \frac{\partial T}{\partial x} \simeq \frac{T_{k+1} - T_k}{h}$$

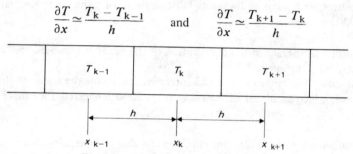

Fig. 7.4. Three segments of a thin rod.

so that a 'model' for $\partial^2 T/\partial x^2$ could then be

$$\frac{\partial^2 T}{\partial x^2} = \frac{\dfrac{T_{k+1} - T_k}{h} - \dfrac{T_k - T_{k-1}}{h}}{h} = \frac{T_{k+1} - 2T_k + T_{k-1}}{h^2}$$

Replacing $\partial^2 T/\partial x^2$ by this model for the steady state situation, gives

$$\frac{T_{k+1} - 2T_k + T_{k-1}}{h^2} = 0 \text{ so that } T_k = \frac{h^2}{2}\left\{ T_{k+1} + T_{k-1} \right\}$$

Crank–Nicholson Equation

except that this equation has to be modified at the ends of the bar to take account of the boundary condition. Divide a bar of unit length into 12 segments, and find the steady state temperature distribution if one end is held at a constant temperature of 100°C while the heat flow at the other end is constant, so that $\partial T/\partial x = 10$ at that point.

The solution is obtained by applying the Crank–Nicholson equation starting at one end of the bar, taking account of the boundary conditions, and working along the bar to the other boundary. This procedure will not give the answer the first time: it must be repeated over and over until the calculated distribution in the bar ceases to change appreciably.

SESSION 8
ARRAYS AND SUBSCRIPTS IN TWO DIMENSIONS

1 Introduction

Once familiarity with arrays of one dimension has been established the extension to higher dimensions is straightforward enough. The use of two subscripts for arrays has very wide application, often in the context of matrix representation.

However programmers often find that dealing with two subscripts simultaneously does not come easily. For this reason a typical two dimensional application is worked through in some detail in this session, the solution of a system of linear equations. It is probable that this session will be found the most demanding of the entire course and so a clear understanding of the previous session is essential. Careful preparation for problem 8.4 is advisable. Although BASIC provides a set of defined matrix operations, these are left to Session 9 so that valuable practice in the use of subscripted variables can be provided here.

2 Arrays and Subscripts of Higher Dimension

BASIC provides for arrays of up to three dimensions. It has been stated that an array in one dimension is an ordered collection of subscripted variables, which form a list or vector, such as:

$$A = \begin{pmatrix} a_1 \\ a_2 \\ a_3 \end{pmatrix}$$

and a member of the list a_i could be represented by a BASIC subscripted variable A(I). The extension to two dimensions is straightforward. Instead of a list or vector, an array of two dimensions forms a table, or matrix, such as:

$$C = \begin{pmatrix} c_{11} & c_{12} & c_{13} \\ c_{21} & c_{22} & c_{23} \\ c_{31} & c_{32} & c_{33} \end{pmatrix}$$

which has double subscripts. The BASIC representation includes both subscripts, separated by a comma. Therefore an item in the table c_{ij} could be represented by the BASIC subscripted variable C(I,J). Similarly a three dimensional form is available, so that t_{ijk} could be called T(I,J,K). Three subscripts is the maximum allowed by BASIC.

As before, any variable used with subscripts is treated as an array. The usage of such a variable throughout the program must be consistent, so that the same variable name with different numbers of subscripts cannot be allowed. If no DIM statement is present, the size of an array is assumed to be 10 in all of its dimensions. Thus the default sizes for arrays of one, two, and three dimensions are 10, 10 by 10, and 10 by 10 respectively.

The form of the DIM statement can be generalized here:

line number **DIM** variable $\begin{pmatrix} up\ to\ three\ integers \\ separated\ by\ commas \\ giving\ size \end{pmatrix}$, variable $\begin{pmatrix} up\ to\ three\ integers \\ separated\ by\ commas \\ giving\ size \end{pmatrix}$ ...

Example `30 DIM Z(25,40)`

defines an array *Z* of size 25 x 40.

3 Problems

PROBLEM 8.1   Write a program to accomplish the scalar product s of two vectors *A* and *B* each of length *n*:

$$s = \sum_{i=1}^{n} a_i b_i$$

Solution   The symbol Σ represents summation, so that the problem requires

$$s = a_1 b_1 + a_2 b_2 + \cdots + a_n b_n$$

Suppose the size of the vectors is to be variable; the program must ask for the size and then ask for the members of the vectors. A flow chart for this could be as in Fig. 8.1. with the corresponding BASIC program

```
10 REM PROGRAM TO MULTIPLY TWO VECTORS A AND B
20 REM FIRST OBTAIN THE LENGTH, N
30 PRINT"TYPE IN THE LENGTH OF THE TWO VECTORS"
40 INPUT N
50 REM NEXT OBTAIN VECTORS A AND B
60 PRINT"NOW TYPE IN"N"ELEMENTS OF VECTOR A, ONE AT A TIME"
70 FOR I = 1 TO N
80 INPUT A(I)
90 NEXT I
100 PRINT"NOW TYPE IN"N"ELEMENTS OF VECTOR B, ONE AT A TIME"
110 FOR I = 1 TO N
120 INPUT B(I)
130 NEXT I
140 REM ACCUMULATE THE SCALAR PRODUCT IN S
150 LET S = 0
160 FOR I = 1 TO N
170 LET S = S+A(I)*B(I)
180 NEXT I
190 PRINT"THE SCALAR PRODUCT IS"S
200 END
```

Note that the vectors are assumed to be less than 10 in length, so no DIM statement is used.

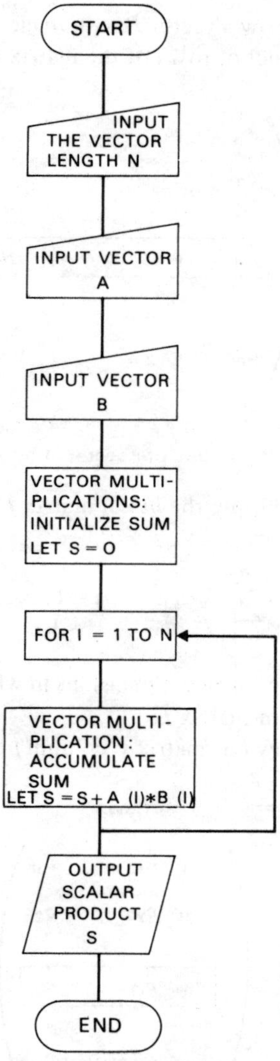

Fig. 8.1. Flow diagram for the scalar product of two vectors.

The arrangements for obtaining the vectors are rather awkward, and better ways are defined later. This program requires only moderate alteration to become the solution to problems 8.2 and 8.3.

PROBLEM 8.2   Write a program to accomplish the vector product B of a $m \times n$ matrix C and an n element vector A. The product B is a vector of m elements:

$$b_i = \sum_{k=1}^{n} c_{ik} a_k \qquad i = 1, \ldots, m$$

The solution of this problem is now a vector B with m elements. The equation shows that b_i is obtained from the scalar product of row i of the matrix C and the vector A, as in Fig. 8.2

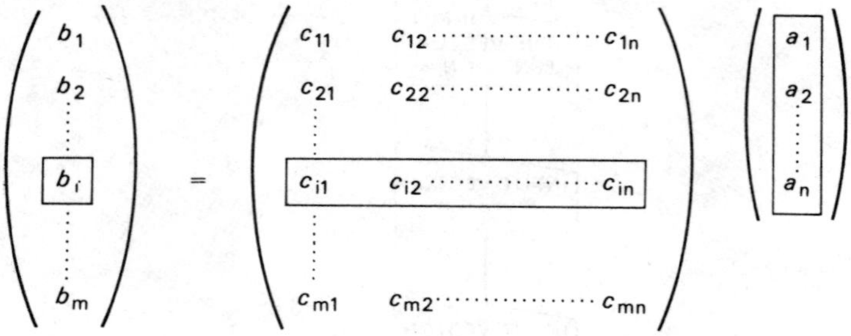

$$\begin{pmatrix} b_1 \\ b_2 \\ \boxed{b_i} \\ \vdots \\ b_m \end{pmatrix} = \begin{pmatrix} c_{11} & c_{12} \cdots\cdots\cdots c_{1n} \\ c_{21} & c_{22} \cdots\cdots\cdots c_{2n} \\ \boxed{c_{i1} \quad c_{i2} \cdots\cdots\cdots c_{in}} \\ \vdots \\ c_{m1} & c_{m2} \cdots\cdots\cdots c_{mn} \end{pmatrix} \begin{pmatrix} a_1 \\ a_2 \\ \vdots \\ a_n \end{pmatrix}$$

$$b_i = c_{i1} a_1 + c_{i2} a_2 + \cdots\cdots + c_{in} a_n$$

Fig. 8.2. Multiplication of a vector A by a matrix C.

PROBLEM 8.3   Write a program to multiply the $m \times n$ matrix C by the $n \times r$ matrix D to give the $m \times r$ result E

$$e_{ij} = \sum_{k=1}^{n} c_{ik} d_{kj}, \qquad \begin{array}{l} i = 1, \ldots m \\ j = 1, \ldots r \end{array}$$

Here the product itself is an array of two dimensions in which e_{ij} is the scalar product of row i of matrix C and column j of matrix E.

A result, e_{ij}, is obtained from row i of matrix C column j of matrix D, as in Fig. 8.3.

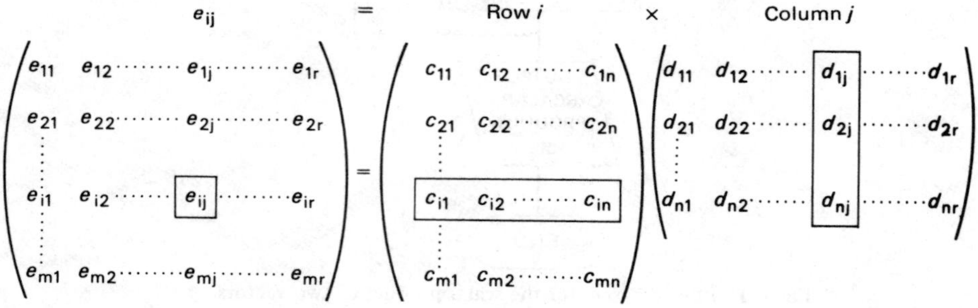

$$e_{ij} \qquad = \qquad \text{Row } i \qquad \times \qquad \text{Column } j$$

$$\begin{pmatrix} e_{11} & e_{12} \cdots e_{1j} \cdots e_{1r} \\ e_{21} & e_{22} \cdots e_{2j} \cdots e_{2r} \\ e_{i1} & e_{i2} \cdots \boxed{e_{ij}} \cdots e_{ir} \\ \vdots \\ e_{m1} & e_{m2} \cdots e_{mj} \cdots e_{mr} \end{pmatrix} = \begin{pmatrix} c_{11} & c_{12} \cdots c_{1n} \\ c_{21} & c_{22} \cdots c_{2n} \\ \boxed{c_{i1} \quad c_{i2} \cdots c_{in}} \\ c_{m1} & c_{m2} \cdots c_{mn} \end{pmatrix} \begin{pmatrix} d_{11} & d_{12} \cdots \boxed{d_{1j}} \cdots d_{1r} \\ d_{21} & d_{22} \cdots \boxed{d_{2j}} \cdots d_{2r} \\ d_{n1} & d_{n2} \cdots \boxed{d_{nj}} \cdots d_{nr} \end{pmatrix}$$

$$e_{ij} = c_{i1} d_{1j} + c_{i2} d_{2j} + \cdots\cdots + c_{in} d_{nj}$$

Fig. 8.3. Multiplication of two matrices.

4 Pre-defined Constants—the DATA, READ, and RESTORE statements

In the above problems, the value of some easier means of giving values to the variables other than typing them each time should have become obvious. BASIC allows a list of constants to be specified in the DATA statement, and these values can be assigned to any variable using the

READ statement. This facility can eliminate the need to type in the same array of data every time a program is run.

The DATA statement has the form:

line number **DATA** *constant, constant, . . .*

The DATA statement itself has no effect on a running BASIC program. Its presence causes the constants to be stored in the computer, and these can be retrieved by the READ statement. Any number of DATA statements can be included in a program, and they can be entered in any position. Their order is important, however, as will be seen. An example of a DATA statement is:

```
10 DATA 38.2,10.5,-9.6
```

The READ statement is used to assign values from the DATA statement to the desired variables. It is written as:

line number **READ** *variable, variable, . . .*

When a running BASIC program encounters the first READ statement, values are read into the named variable from the DATA statements in order and in one-to-one correspondence with the requirements of the READ statement.

Exercise   Try the program

```
10 DATA 38.2,10.5,-9.6
20 READ A,B,C
30 PRINT A,B,C
40 END
```

Exercise   Try the program

```
10 DATA 38.2,10.5,-9.6
20 FOR I = 1 TO 3
30 READ X(I)
40 NEXT I
50 PRINT X(1),X(2),X(3)
60 END
```

Successive READ statements encountered by the running program carry on through the DATA statements. Thus if only part of a DATA statement is used by a given READ, then the next READ starts from the next value. It could be said that a pointer moves through the DATA statement constants as values are used by READ statements.

Exercise   Try the program

```
10 DATA 38.2,10.5,-9.6
20 FOR I = 1 TO 3
30 READ Z
40 PRINT Z
50 NEXT I
60 END
```

In this program, the DATA pointer is initially at the beginning of the list:

NEXT VALUE
   ↓
  38.2   10.5   −9.6

so that when I = 1, the READ Z statement assigns 38.2 to Z, and moves the pointer along:

                      NEXT VALUE
                          ↓
38.2   10.5   −9.6

so that when I = 2, 10.5 is assigned to Z and the pointer moves again:

                                   NEXT VALUE
                                     ↓
38.2   10.5   −9.6

Similarly, if more variables are requested by a READ statement than are given by one DATA statement, the next DATA statement according to line number is taken. Thus the order of occurrence of DATA statements is significant. It is incorrect to ask for more constants than are present in all the DATA statements.

EXERCISE   Try the program

```
10 DATA 38.2
20 FOR I = 1 TO 3
30 DATA 10.5
40 READ X(I)
50 DATA -9.6
60 NEXT I
70 PRINT X(1),X(2),X(3)
80 END
```

The RESTORE statement returns the pointer to the first constant given in the first DATA statement, so that all the given data can be re-used. There is no direct means of returning to the middle of the DATA list, but it is possible to return to the beginning with the RESTORE and read through to the desired place, for example in a FOR and NEXT loop.

RESTORE has the form:

line number **RESTORE**

EXERCISE   Try the following program

```
10 DATA 1,2,3
20 FOR J = 1 TO 2
30 FOR I = 1 TO 3
40 READ X
50 PRINT X;
60 NEXT I
70 RESTORE
80 NEXT J
90 END
```

The behaviour of the pointer in this program is then:

First:
J = 1	↓		
I = 1	1	2	3
J = 1		↓	
I = 2	1	2	3
J = 1			↓
I = 3	1	2	3

RESTORE
J = 2	↓		
I = 1	1	2	3
J = 2		↓	
I = 2	1	2	3
J = 2			↓
I = 3	1	2	3

RESTORE
↓		
1	2	3

5 Problem—solution of Linear Equations by Gaussian Elimination

There are many different methods for solving systems of simultaneous linear equations using digital computers, and the choice of a method depends on efficiency, accuracy, reliability, and simplicity. The method of Gaussian elimination is a straightforward method, and is the one normally used in hand calculations:

Suppose the equations are:

$$a_{11}x_1 + a_{12}x_2 + a_{13}x_3 = y_1 \tag{1}$$

$$a_{21}x_1 + a_{22}x_2 + a_{23}x_3 = y_2 \tag{2}$$

$$a_{31}x_1 + a_{32}x_2 + a_{33}x_3 = y_3 \tag{3}$$

The first step in the solution by Gaussian elimination is to eliminate variable x_1 from two of these equations and so produce two new equations in the two unknown variables x_2 and x_3. To accomplish this, subtract row (1) times a_{21}/a_{11} from row (2) and subtract row (1) times a_{31}/a_{11} from row (3), a_{11} is used throughout this step as what is called the pivot element, as follows:

(2) $- a_{21}/a_{11}$ (1)   gives a new equation

$$b_{22}x_2 + b_{23}x_3 = y_2' \tag{4}$$

where $b_{22} = a_{22} - \dfrac{a_{21}a_{12}}{a_{11}}$

$$b_{23} = a_{23} - \frac{a_{21}a_{13}}{a_{11}}$$

and $y_2' = y_2 - \dfrac{a_{21}y_1}{a_{11}}$

similarly,

(3) $- a_{31}/a_{11}$ (1)   gives a new equation

$$b_{32}x_2 + b_{33}x_3 = y_3' \tag{5}$$

The next step is to eliminate the variable x_2. To do this take equation (5) and subtract from it b_{32}/b_{22} times equation (4); b_{22} is the pivot element:

(5) $- b_{32}/b_{22}$ (4)   gives a new equation

$$c_{33}x_3 = y_3'' \tag{6}$$

The entire system of equations has been reduced to:

$$a_{11}x_1 + a_{12}x_2 + a_{13}x_3 = y_1 \tag{1}$$
$$b_{22}x_2 + b_{23}x_3 = y_2' \tag{4}$$
$$c_{23}x_3 = y_3'' \tag{6}$$

and the answer can be found by working backwards using a process of back substitution:

$$x_3 = \frac{y_3''}{c_{33}}$$

$$x_2 = \frac{y_2' - b_{23}x_3}{b_{22}}$$

$$x_1 = \frac{y_1 - a_{12}x_2 - a_{13}x_3}{a_{11}}$$

It is easy to translate this into a computer program. The coefficients of the original system of equation form a 3 x 3 array for the left hand side, and the right hand forms an array of one dimension, length three. A program can then be written which works its way through the array replacing the coefficients as variables are eliminated. The arrays are transformed as the solution proceeds:

initially
$$\begin{pmatrix} a_{11} a_{12} a_{13} \\ a_{21} a_{22} a_{23} \\ a_{31} a_{32} a_{33} \end{pmatrix} \quad \text{and} \quad \begin{pmatrix} y_1 \\ y_2 \\ y_3 \end{pmatrix}$$

after stage 1
$$\begin{pmatrix} a_{11} a_{12} a_{13} \\ 0 \ b_{22} b_{23} \\ 0 \ b_{32} b_{33} \end{pmatrix} \quad \text{and} \quad \begin{pmatrix} y_1 \\ y_2' \\ y_3' \end{pmatrix}$$

after stage 2
$$\begin{pmatrix} a_{11} a_{12} a_{13} \\ 0 \ b_{22} b_{23} \\ 0 \ 0 \ c_{33} \end{pmatrix} \quad \text{and} \quad \begin{pmatrix} y_1 \\ y_2' \\ y_3'' \end{pmatrix}$$

The answer can be derived by back-substitution. This method makes efficient use of storage because the transformed rows can replace the original rows in the same array. However, there is one pitfall in this, which will be pointed out.

Supposing now there are N equations and an array A and a vector Y are used, then the algorithm as illustrated in Fig. 8.4 can be stated:

For each column K from 1 to N−1
    For each row I from K+1 to N
        Operate on Y(I) by
            letting Y(I) = Y(I) − Y(K)*A(I, K)/A(K, K)
        and also for J from K to N operate on A(I, J) by
            letting A(I, J) = A(I, J) − A(K, J)*A(I, K)/A(K, K)

A(K, K) is used in all the calculations in eliminating column K, and is called the pivot element. There is a dangerous pitfall in this procedure, for A(I, J) when J = K, is the first element of row I to be eliminated. But the old value of A(I, K) is still needed for the remainder of row I. Therefore if the new A(I, K) is allowed to replace the old one immediately, the method will fail. There are

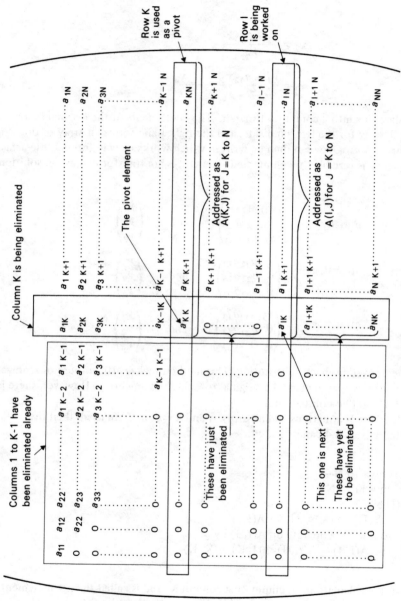

Fig. 8.4. The state of an array in the midst of Gaussian elimination. Row K is used as pivot for the elimination of column K, which has progressed to row I.

two ways around this. One is to run the appropriate loops backwards as one can do in BASIC, and the other is to use an intermediate variable Z,

$$\text{letting } Z = A(I, K)/A(K, K)$$

at the beginning of a row, and using the formulae

$$Y(I) = Y(I) - Y(K)*Z$$
$$\text{and} \quad A(I, J) = A(I, J) - A(K, J)*Z$$

This has the advantage of added efficiency, since the time taken by subscripting would be a significant factor in the speed of this method, and the number of subscripts used in the inner loop has been reduced.

Assuming a vector X is used for the answer, the back-substitution procedure is:

$$X(N) = Y(N)/A(N, N)$$

and from each row K from N−1 to 1,

$$X(K) = \frac{Y(K) - \sum_{J=K+1}^{N} A(K, J)*X(J)}{A(K, K)}$$

The flowchart for this entire procedure is shown in Fig. 8.5.

PROBLEM 8.4   Write a program to solve N linear equations in N unknowns by the Gaussian elimination method. Print out the array of coefficients after each column has been eliminated, and solve the equations:

$$2x + 10y - 6z + 4u + 8v = 8$$
$$-3x - 12y - 9z + 6u + 3v = 3$$
$$-x + y - 34z + 15u + 18v = 29$$
$$4x + 18y + 4u + 14v = -2$$
$$5x + 26y - 19z + 25u + 36v = 23$$

Use 5 DATA statements to set up the coefficients, and another for the vector on the right hand side.

6 Problem—Interchanging Rows of Linear Equations

In the use of the Gaussian elimination method, a complete disaster will occur if any pivot element A(K, K) becomes zero because division by zero is not valid. Even if not zero, large errors can be introduced if any pivot element turns out to be very small compared to the other coefficients.

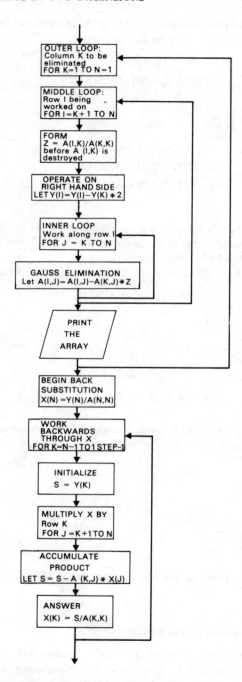

Fig. 8.5. Flow diagram for Gaussian elimination and back-substitution.

The pivot element for a given column elimination after the first is itself the result of earlier calculations, so that a small pivot element can arise unpredictably at any stage by subtraction of nearly equal numbers, and ruin the solution.

However the use of 'pivotal condensation' can help to minimize the effect of small coefficients by moving them to another row so they are not used as the pivot element. It is obvious that interchanging two rows of the coefficient array is equivalent to changing the order of the equations, and therefore has no effect on the answer. Thus if the coefficient of largest magnitude in column K between rows K and N is always used as the pivot, the seriousness of this kind of error is reduced. Hence for each choice of K, row K can be interchanged another row below it to obtain the pivot element of largest magnitude. The corresponding values on the right hand side must also be interchanged.

PROBLEM 8.5   Write a program to solve N linear equations in N unknowns using Gaussian elimination with row interchanges. Print out sufficient intermediate results to be able to follow the interchanges, because errors in the first attempt are very likely.

7 Summary Notes on Session 8

(a) Arrays of one dimension are written as variable with a single subscript, as $A(I)$. If not mentioned in a DIM statement, the size is taken to be 10.

(b) Arrays of two dimensions are written as a variable with two subscripts, as $A(I, J)$. If not mentioned in a DIM statement the size is taken to be 10×10.

(c) Arrays of three dimensions are written as a variable with three subscripts, as $A(I, J, K)$. If not mentioned in a DIM statement the size is taken to be $10 \times 10 \times 10$.

(d) BASIC allows a maximum of three subscripts.

(e) The same variable name cannot be used with different numbers of subscripts.

(f) A subscript can be any expression. Allowed values of subscripts are between 1 and the array size. If the subscript expression gives a non-integer result, the subscript is truncated. Thus $A(3.78)$ means $A(3)$.

(g) The DIM statement specifies a size other than 10 for arrays:

line number **DIM** *subscripted variable, subscripted variable* . . .

In the DIM statement, the subscripts must be integer numbers, which specify the array size.

(h) The DATA statement has the form:

line number **DATA** *constant, constant* . . .

for example

```
10 DATA 38.2,10.5,-9.6
```

The constants given in the DATA statement are stored in the computer in order. Successive DATA statements add to the list in order.

(i) The READ statement assigns values from the DATA list to variables:

line number **READ** *variable, variable* . . .

When the READ statement is encountered the values from the DATA list are assigned one by one to the named variables. Successive READ statements continue through the data list.

(j) The RESTORE statement causes the next READ statement to return to the beginning of the DATA list:

line number **RESTORE**

8 Supplementary Problems

It would be good form to cast as much of these problems as possible into subroutine form.

PROBLEM 8.6   In problem 8.5 it was seen that interchanging rows of systems of equations had no effect on the solution. Columns can also be moved without affecting the numerical value of the answer, but the order of the variables in the result is changed. However a one dimensional array containing the column numbers could be used to keep track of the column rearrangement, by interchanging elements of the array whenever columns are interchanged, and using this information to restore the final answer to correct sequence.

Write a program to solve a system of linear equations by Gaussian elimination with full interchange of rows and columns (called pivotal condensation), so that the pivot element is always the one of largest available magnitude.

PROBLEM 8.7   A useful variation of the Gaussian Elimination method can give the inverse matrix as well as the solution of the equation. A set of equations:

$$b + c + d = -1$$
$$4b + 2c + d = -6$$
$$16b + 4c + d = -63$$

could be represented by the matrix equation

$$A\,x = y \quad \text{or} \quad \begin{pmatrix} 1 & 1 & 1 \\ 4 & 2 & 1 \\ 16 & 4 & 1 \end{pmatrix} \begin{pmatrix} b \\ c \\ d \end{pmatrix} = \begin{pmatrix} -1 \\ -6 \\ -63 \end{pmatrix}$$

The inverse of A, called A^{-1}, is such the solution of the equation is $x = A^{-1} y$ and A^{-1} always exists if the equations have a solution.

The inverse matrix can be found by the Gauss–Jordan method, which is almost identical to the Gaussian elimination method, except that each column is eliminated entirely except for the diagonal member.

Two matrices are operated on simultaneously, the coefficient matrix and a unit matrix:

$$\begin{pmatrix} a_{11} & a_{12} & \cdots & a_{1n} \\ a_{21} & a_{22} & \cdots & a_{2n} \\ & \cdot & & \\ & \cdot & & \\ & \cdot & & \\ a_{n1} & a_{n2} & \cdots & a_{nn} \end{pmatrix} \quad \text{and} \quad \begin{pmatrix} 1 & 0 & \cdots & 0 \\ 0 & 1 & \cdots & 0 \\ & \cdot & & \\ & \cdot & & \\ & \cdot & & \\ 0 & 0 & \cdots & 1 \end{pmatrix}$$
$$ A I$$

In the elimination, every operation that is performed on $A(I, J)$ is also done to $I(I, J)$, and if each row is also divided by the remaining diagonal element, the two matrices become:

$$\begin{pmatrix} 1 & 0 & \dots & 0 \\ 0 & 1 & \dots & 0 \\ & & \cdot & \\ & & \cdot & \\ & & \cdot & \\ 0 & 0 & \dots & 1 \end{pmatrix} \text{ and } \begin{pmatrix} & \\ & A^{-1} & \\ & \end{pmatrix}$$

a unit matrix   the inverse of A

Find the inverse of $\begin{pmatrix} 1 & 1 & 1 \\ 4 & 2 & 1 \\ 16 & 4 & 1 \end{pmatrix}$ and so solve the given equation.

PROBLEM 8.8   Rewrite the program of problem 8.7 to use full pivotal condensation.

PROBLEM 8.9   A linear differential equation can be represented in matrix form:

The equation

$$\frac{d^2 y}{dt^2} + 2 \frac{dy}{dt} + 5y = 1$$

can be reduced to $\dfrac{dy_1}{dt} = y_2$ and $\dfrac{dy_2}{dt} = -5y_1 - 2y_2 + 1$

which could be written

$$\begin{pmatrix} \dfrac{dy_1}{dt} \\[2mm] \dfrac{dy_2}{dt} \end{pmatrix} = \begin{pmatrix} 0 & 1 \\ -5 & -2 \end{pmatrix} \begin{pmatrix} y_1 \\ y_2 \end{pmatrix} + \begin{pmatrix} 0 \\ 1 \end{pmatrix}$$

Write a subroutine which uses the Runge–Kutta technique (problem 4.10) to solve a system of linear equations using matrix form. Solve the equation:

$$\frac{d^3 y}{dt^3} + 3 \frac{d^2 y}{dt^3} + 2 \frac{dy}{dt} = 0$$

for $y(0) = -1$, $\dot{y}(0) = -1$ and $\ddot{y}(0) = -1$. Plot the three curves for y, $\dot{y}$, and $\ddot{y}$ simultaneously. Try different values of step size; the solution will be wildly unstable if too large a step is chosen.

PROBLEM 8.10   Using an array of two dimensions the heat conduction equation can be solved in time and space. The equation of heat conduction in a thin rod as shown in Fig. 8.6 is

$$\frac{\partial^2 T}{\partial x^2} = \frac{\partial T}{\partial t}$$

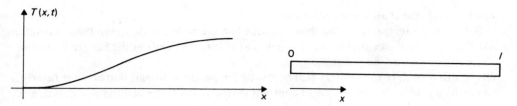

Fig. 8.6. Temperature distribution in a thin rod.

Suppose the rod is divided into a number of discrete segments of width h, and time is also divided into segments of duration Δt. Then

$$T(x, t) = T(kh, l\Delta t)$$

and the temperature distribution in space and time can be represented in an array of two dimensions as Fig. 8.7.

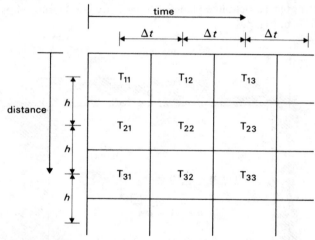

Fig. 8.7. Arrangement of Temperature distribution as a function of distance and time in an array of two dimensions.

Considering a cell in the centre of the array, the heat conduction equation could be modelled by

$$\frac{T_{k+1,\ell} - 2T_{k\ell} + T_{k-1,\ell}}{h^2} = \frac{T_{k,\ell+1} - T_{k,\ell-1}}{2\Delta t}$$

From which

$$T_{k\ell} = \frac{T_{k+1,\ell} + T_{k-1,\ell}}{2} - \frac{h^2}{4\Delta t}(T_{k,\ell+1} - T_{k,\ell-1})$$

Crank–Nicholson Equation

suitably modified at all 4 array boundaries.

Solve for the temperature distribution in the bar, given that at time zero the temperature is $0°C$ except for the central segment which is at $100°C$. The ends of the bar are insulated, which means that $\partial T / \partial x = 0$ at the ends.

The fourth boundary of the array represents the temperature distribution at some future time, which eventually will be one of constant temperature. If the number and duration of time increments is sufficient, then the condition $\dfrac{\partial T}{\partial t} = 0$ will not be appreciably in error.

As in problem 7.10, application of the model equation will not lead to the correct results directly; the calculation must be repeated iteratively until the result ceases to change appreciably from one iteration to the next.

PROBLEM 8.11   Solve the Laplace Equation

$$\frac{\partial^2 u}{\partial x^2} + \frac{\partial^2 u}{\partial y^2} = 0$$

for the electrostatic potential field in a plane with perfectly conducting edges and a dipolar source at the centre as in Fig. 8.8.

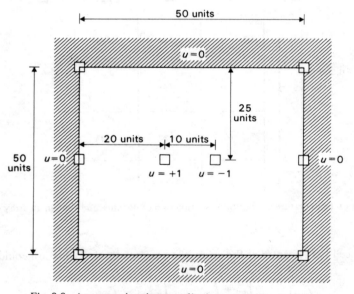

Fig. 8.8. An approximation to a dipolar source of potential.

For efficiency, the solution should take account of the symmetry of the configuration. The result could very neatly be represented by plotting isopotential lines on the printer.

SESSION 9
MATRIX OPERATIONS

1 Introduction

There are a number of standard operations on matrices which BASIC provides for convenience in matrix manipulation. These can save considerable programming effort, by replacing the many lines of program which would otherwise be required.

All the facilities discussed up to this point should be available in any respectable implementation of BASIC. Nearly every version of BASIC provides the matrix facilities described here, but in some small computers they may be deleted to overcome space restrictions. From this point forward, it is possible that some of the features described may not be included in a particular BASIC system.

2 Matrices and Vectors

An array of one dimension is a column vector. The statement:

```
10 DIM A(3)
```

defines a column vector:

$$\begin{pmatrix} A(1) \\ A(2) \\ A(3) \end{pmatrix}$$

An array of two dimensions is a matrix. The statement:

```
10 DIM B(3,3)
```

defines a matrix:

$$\begin{pmatrix} B(1,1) & B(1,2) & B(1,3) \\ B(2,1) & B(2,2) & B(2,3) \\ B(3,1) & B(3,2) & B(3,3) \end{pmatrix}$$

Therefore the column vector is a special case of the matrix, for the statement:

    10 DIM C(3,1)

defines:

$$\begin{pmatrix} C(1,1) \\ C(2,1) \\ C(3,1) \end{pmatrix}$$

which could be the same as the column vector as above except that as far as **BASIC** is concerned it has two dimensions.

However the statement:

    10 DIM D(1,3)

defines a row vector:

$$(D(1,1) \quad D(1,2) \quad D(1,3))$$

Therefore a column vector could be an array of either one or two dimensions, but a row vector must be given two dimensions.

3 Facilities for Input and Output of Matrices—MAT INPUT and MAT PRINT*

Using the ordinary PRINT and INPUT statements, an awkward looping arrangement is required for input and output of matrices or vectors, as in problem 8.1. Fortunately, however, BASIC provides special facilities for these operations. The MAT PRINT statement has the form:

line number **MAT PRINT** $\frac{array}{variable}$ *delimiter* $\frac{array}{variable}$ *delimiter* . . .

This statement causes the named variables to be printed out as matrices, one row of one matrix at a time. The delimiter after the variable name is a semicolon or comma which specifies how the elements of the named matrix are to be spaced. The delimiter does not affect the next line: a row always begins on a new line.

* The MAT INPUT facility is omitted from at least one version of BASIC known to the author. Strangely, all the other matrix statements are present in the particular small computer.

In similar fashion, the **MAT INPUT** statement asks for data to be typed in at the terminal one row at a time. A prompting '?' is typed by the computer when each row is required. It is written:

line number **MAT INPUT** *array variable' array variable' array variable'* . . .

A useful additional facility which the **MAT INPUT** statement shares with some other matrix operations is the ability to redimension a matrix. Even if the matrix is mentioned in a DIM statement, it can have its size changed by the **MAT INPUT** statement, as long as the new size is smaller than the original size specified by a DIM statement (or by default). The number of dimensions cannot be changed. By writing

```
1 Ø  MAT  INPUT  A(5,3)
```

and assuming *A* was at first an array or two dimensions with at least 15 members in all, then the dimensions of matrix *A* are changed to 5 x 3. The redimensioning subscripts could also be expressions, as

```
1 Ø  MAT  INPUT  B(I↑J,K+L)
```

in which case the subscripts are truncated if they are not integers.

EXERCISE   Using the MAT INPUT and MAT PRINT facilities do the following:

(i) Read in a 3 x 3 matrix and type it out using the comma as a delimiter.
(ii) Read in a 3 x 5 matrix and type it out using the semicolon as a delimiter.
(iii) Read in and type out two matrices using one MAT INPUT and one MAT PRINT statement.
(iv) Read in and type out a row vector.

4 Definition of Special Matrices—MAT ZER, MAT CON and MAT IDN

Three facilities are available for defining special matrices, and all three can redimension the matrix involved. The MAT . . . ZER facility is typical:

line number **MAT** *variable* = **ZER**

This form of MAT . . . ZER defines the array variable named to be all zeros. For redimensioning one form is:

line number **MAT** *variable* = **ZER** (*expression a, expression b*)

which defines a zero matrix of dimensions INT (*expression a*) x INT (*expression b*). As with the
MAT INPUT statement, a matrix cannot be redimensioned as larger than its original size (given
by a DIM statement, or by default as 10 in each dimension). The number of dimensions applicable
to an array must always be consistent.

Examples

```
10 MAT X = ZER
```

The array X is defined as all zeros, and its size is not changed

```
55 MAT Y = ZER(5)
```

The array Y, which must be of one dimension, is defined as all zeros and is redimensioned to
length 5. The size of Y must originally have been 5 or greater.

```
15 MAT A = ZER(Z↑2,P+Q)
```

The array A, which must be of two dimensions, is defined to be all zeros and is redimensioned
to $Z↑2$ by P + Q. The expressions for the new dimensions are truncated to integers if necessary,
and must give positive values which are not greater than the original dimensions.

A similar facility is the MAT . . . CON statement, which defines an array of all ones with
exactly the same forms of redimensioning as MAT . . . ZER.

EXERCISE   Verify that the MAT . . . ZER and MAT . . . CON statements work as described, by
investigating the effect of redimensioning on a subsequent MAT PRINT instruction.

The MAT . . . IDN statement is used to define an identity or unit matrix, which must be square
to be valid, so the redimensioning is restricted. The statement

```
25 MAT B = IDN
```

requires that B is already a square matrix of two dimensions. The statement

```
50 MAT A = IDN(5,5)
```

requires that the array A be of two dimensions. If the size of A was not less than 5 x 5 originally
then A becomes the unit matrix:

$$A = \begin{pmatrix} 1 & 0 & 0 & 0 & 0 \\ 0 & 1 & 0 & 0 & 0 \\ 0 & 0 & 1 & 0 & 0 \\ 0 & 0 & 0 & 1 & 0 \\ 0 & 0 & 0 & 0 & 1 \end{pmatrix}$$

As with all the statements of BASIC, violation of the rules governing these facilities will result in the printing of a diagnostic message on the terminal.

5 Matrix Algebra

Addition, subtraction or multiplication of matrices would require FOR − NEXT loops if there were not special statements available. All the algebraic operations on the matrices are meaningful only if the arrays 'conform' for the particular operation desired. The meaning of conformability will be explained for each operation.

(i) Addition and Subtraction

Matrix addition or subtraction is supported by BASIC. The statement

```
34 MAT  A  =  B+C
```

results in the arrays (which could be of one or two dimensions) B and C being added together element by element to form the array A. Therefore conformability of A, B, and C, is required and this means that they must all have the same dimensions. The result is that

$$a_{ij} = b_{ij} + c_{ij}$$

Similarly, the statement

```
35 MAT  D  =  B-C
```

produces a result in which

$$d_{ij} = b_{ij} - c_{ij}$$

The general form of these facilities is then

line number **MAT** *variable a = variable b ± variable c*

It is possible for the variable on the left hand side to be one of those named on the right hand side. Therefore the statement

```
51 MAT  A  =  A+B
```

is a valid replacement statement for array A.

(ii) Multiplication by a scalar

Scalar multiplication is also supported in the form:

line number **MAT** *variable a = (expression) ∗ variable b*

The expression written in brackets gives a scalar multiplier which is applied to every element of the named array variable b, and the results are placed in array variable a. Again, conformability means that the arrays must have the same dimensions. The replacement statement

```
99 MAT A = (10)*A
```

is valid, and produces a result in which all elements of the array A are multiplied by 10. The statement

```
25 MAT B = (1)*A
```

is a very convenient way of saving or transferring matrix A into matrix B.

(iii) Matrix Multiplication

Matrix multiplication has more complicated requirements for conformability by the nature of the operation. The difference between column and row vectors becomes important. The general matrix multiplication of a $m \times n$ array C by a $n \times r$ array D produces a $m \times r$ result, E in which

$$e_{ij} = \sum_{k=1}^{r} c_{ik}\, d_{jk} \qquad \begin{aligned} i &= 1, \ldots m \\ j &= 1, \ldots r \end{aligned}$$

An element e_{ij} is obtained by multiplication of row i of matrix C by column j of matrix D. This is relatively easy to remember, because c_{ij} is itself in the ith row and jth column of matrix E as in Fig. 9.1.

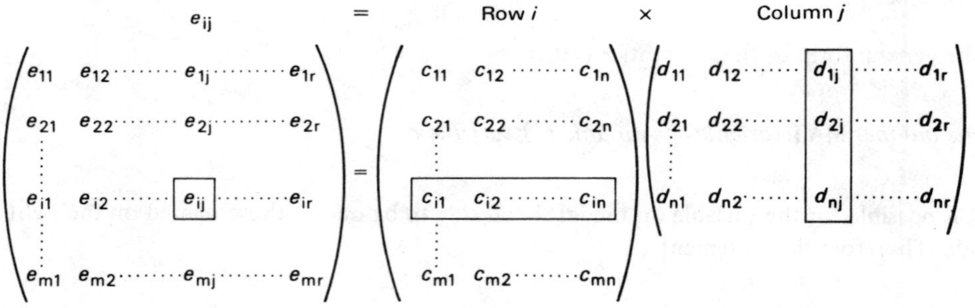

$$e_{ij} = c_{i1}\, d_{1j} + c_{i2}\, d_{2j} + \cdots + c_{in}\, d_{nj}$$

Fig. 9.1. Multiplication of matrices.

For this operation to conform, the number of entries in a row of A must be the same as in a column of B.

Therefore, A and B have the common size n and the order of multiplication is important. The result is of size $m \times r$.

A matrix multiplication statement in BASIC can be written as:

$$\text{line number } \mathbf{MAT} \; \underset{variable}{array} c = \underset{variable}{array} a * \underset{variable}{array} b$$

where the three variables name three different arrays, for example

```
69 MAT E = C*D
```

Here, matrices C and D must have a common dimension, which is the second one of C and the first of D. The result E must be of a dimension which fits the first of C and the last size of D. Therefore, it can be seen that C must be of two dimensions, and E and D could be of one or two dimensions. Thus vector multiplication is a special case and can be done with this MAT statement. The possible situations are:

$MAT\ E$ Result Matrix	=	C First Multiplier	*	D Second Multiplier
Two Dimensions $m \times r$		Two Dimensions $m \times n$		Two Dimensions $n \times r$
A Column Vector = One Dimension m or Two Dimensions $m \times 1$		Two Dimensions $m \times n$		A Column Vector = One Dimension n or Two Dimensions $n \times 1$
A Row Vector = Two Dimensions $1 \times r$		A Row Vector = Two Dimensions $1 \times n$		Two Dimensions $n \times r$
A Scalar Product = One Dimension 1 or Two Dimensions 1×1		A Row Vector = Two Dimensions $1 \times n$		A Column Vector = Two Dimensions $n \times 1$ or One Dimension n

Note then even if a product is a scalar, it must be an array name dimensioned 1 or 1×1. In matrix multiplication, the product *cannot* replace one of the multipliers. Thus a different matrix name must appear on the left hand side.

6 Pre-Defined Matrices—the MAT READ statement

In order to define arrays using the ordinary READ statement, FOR . . . NEXT loops have been used. However, it is possible to use a MAT READ statement in conjunction with DATA lists (and RESTORE statements) to reduce the length of program. To read a list of matrices from the DATA list simply write:

$$\text{line number } \mathbf{MAT\ READ} \; \underset{a}{array} variable, \underset{b}{array} variable$$

When this statement is encountered, *array a* is filled from the DATA list in row order, then *array b*, etc. Redimensioning is allowed, as in the example:

```
35 MAT READ A(3,3)
```

The matrix A is filled from the DATA list, and is redefined to be a 3 x 3 array. A must have originally had at least 9 elements, and must always have had two dimensions.

7 Problem—Iterative Solution of Equations

In some situations, an iterative method for solving equations may produce an acceptable result faster than a direct solution, such as the Gaussian elimination method.

Suppose a system of n equations is represented by

$$Ax = y$$

where A is a matrix of coefficients, y is the right hand side vector, and x is the array of unknowns.

First form a matrix

$$D^{-1} = \begin{pmatrix} 1/a_{11} & & & & 0 \\ & 1/a_{22} & & & \\ & & \cdot & & \\ & & & \cdot & \\ & & & & \cdot \\ 0 & & & & 1/a_{nn} \end{pmatrix}$$

which is a diagonal matrix containing the reciprocals of the diagonal elements of A.

Then find the product

$$C = D^{-1} y$$

which will be a column vector which is a very crude estimate of the solution of the equation. In fact

$$c_i = y_i/a_{ii}$$

and would be the correct answer if A was purely diagonal. Form two further matrices, L and U called the lower and upper matrices.

$$L = \begin{pmatrix} 0 & 0 & 0 & \cdots & 0 & 0 \\ a_{21} & 0 & 0 & \cdots & 0 & 0 \\ a_{31} & a_{32} & 0 & \cdots & 0 & 0 \\ \cdot & \cdot & \cdot & & \cdot & \cdot \\ \cdot & \cdot & \cdot & & \cdot & \cdot \\ \cdot & \cdot & \cdot & & \cdot & \cdot \\ a_{n1} & a_{n2} & a_{n3} & \cdots & a_{nn-1} & a_{nn} \end{pmatrix}$$

i.e. the elements of A below the diagonal, and

$$U = \begin{pmatrix} 0 & a_{12} & a_{13} & \cdots & a_{1n-1} & a_{1n} \\ 0 & 0 & a_{23} & \cdots & a_{2n-1} & a_{2n} \\ 0 & 0 & 0 & \cdots & a_{3n-1} & a_{3n} \\ \cdot & \cdot & \cdot & & \cdot & \cdot \\ \cdot & \cdot & \cdot & & \cdot & \cdot \\ \cdot & \cdot & \cdot & & \cdot & \cdot \\ 0 & 0 & 0 & \cdots & a_{nn-1} & a_{nn} \end{pmatrix}$$

i.e. the elements of A above the diagonal.

Two possible iterative solutions to find $\mathbf{x}$ are:

$$\mathbf{x}_{k+1} = -D^{-1}(L + U)\mathbf{x}_k + D^{-1}\mathbf{y}$$
$$= D^{-1}\{\mathbf{y} - (L + U)\mathbf{x}_k\}$$
$$\text{the Jacobi method}$$

or $$\mathbf{x}_{k+1} = -D^{-1}L\mathbf{x}_{k+1} - D^{-1}U\mathbf{x}_k + D^{-1}\mathbf{y}$$
$$= D^{-1}\{\mathbf{y} - L\mathbf{x}_{k+1} - U\mathbf{x}_k\}$$
$$\text{the Gauss–Seidel method}$$

where $\mathbf{x}_{k+1}$ is the new estimate of $\mathbf{x}$, and $\mathbf{x}_k$ is the previous one. Either of these methods will converge under favourable conditions.

PROBLEM 9.1   Using matrix operations, solve by the Jacobi iteration to three decimal places:

$$A\mathbf{x} = \mathbf{y}$$

where

$$A = \begin{pmatrix} 4 & 0 & 1 & 1 \\ 0 & 4 & 0 & 1 \\ 1 & 0 & 4 & 0 \\ 0 & 0 & 0 & 4 \end{pmatrix}$$

and

$$\mathbf{y} = \begin{pmatrix} 1 \\ 2 \\ 3 \\ 4 \end{pmatrix}$$

8 Matrix Inversion—the MAT . . . INV and MAT . . . TRN statements

If the system of equations

$$A\mathbf{x} = \mathbf{y}$$

has a solution, then there exists a matrix called the inverse of A, or A^{-1}, which gives the solution directly as

$$x = A^{-1}y$$

Thus finding the inverse matrix is one way of solving systems of equations, and the inverse has many other uses as well.

Taking the equation:

$$Ax = y$$

and premultiplying by A^{-1} gives

$$A^{-1}Ax = A^{-1}y$$

But $x = A^{-1}y$, and so

$$A^{-1}A = I$$

where I is the identity matrix.

BASIC provides the MAT . . . INV statement as a means of inverting matrices, and so the solution of equations and many other problems are simplified. The form of this is:

line number **MAT** variable a = INV (variable b)

When this is encountered, the matrix named by *variable b* is inverted and the inverse placed in the matrix named by *variable a*. It follows that both matrices must be square ($n \times n$) and of the same size. The same matrix may not appear on both sides of the statement.

Example 37 MAT B = INV(A)

The square matrix A is inverted, and the result placed in B.

The final BASIC facility for matrices is that of transposition. The transpose of a matrix A is a matrix B where:

$$b_{ij} = a_{ji}$$

To accomplish this in BASIC write:

line number MAT B = TRN(A)

Both matrices must be square and of the same size. The same name may not be used on both sides.

9 Problems

PROBLEM 9.2   Using the MAT . . . INV statement, solve the equations of problems 9.1. Check the inverse by multiplication to produce an identity matrix.

PROBLEM 9.3   Find the inverse of the matrix:

$$A = \begin{pmatrix} 28.45 & 0.74 & 4.63 & 6.01 \\ -5.72 & -16.35 & 2.81 & 1.59 \\ 0.48 & 1.91 & 17.05 & 7.77 \\ 5.40 & -2.15 & -8.83 & 32.30 \end{pmatrix}$$

by using the iterative formula

$$B_{r+1} = B_r(I + E_r)$$

where

$$E_r = I - AB_r$$

A = original matrix

B_r = rth estimate of the inverse of A

Take

$$\begin{pmatrix} 0.035 & 0 & 0 & 0 \\ 0 & -0.06 & 0 & 0 \\ 0 & 0 & 0.06 & 0 \\ 0 & 0 & 0 & 0.03 \end{pmatrix}$$

as the original estimate of the inverse matrix, and stop the iteration procedure when the absolute value of the trace of $(E_r^T * E_r) < 0.01$, where E_r^T denotes the transpose of E_r. The trace of a square matrix is the sum of its diagonal elements. Check the answer by using the INV function to evaluate the inverse of A. Also check A^{-1} by multiplying it by A, to produce an approximate identity matrix.

10 Summary Notes on Session 9

(a) The MAT PRINT statement

line number **MAT PRINT** $\frac{array}{name}$ *delimiter* $\frac{array}{name}$ *delimiter* . . .

prints the named arrays of one or two dimensions beginning each row with a new line, and separating elements according to the given delimiter (comma or semicolon)

(b) The MAT INPUT statement

line number **MAT INPUT** $\frac{array,\ array}{name\ name}$ . . .

asks for the named arrays of one or two dimensions in order, one row at a time. Redimensioning is allowed (see note (d)).

(c) Special matrices. Operations for arrays of one or two dimensions. Redimensioning is allowed (see note (d))

line number **MAT** $\frac{array}{name}$ = **ZER**

defines an array of all zeros.

line number **MAT** $\frac{array}{name}$ = **CON**

defines an array of all ones

line number **MAT** $\frac{array}{name}$ = **IDN**

defines a unit matrix (identity matrix). The matrix so defined must be square.

(d) Matrix redimensioning is allowed by several of the matrix statements. The number of dimensions cannot be changed, and the original total number of elements cannot be exceeded (whether specified in a DIM statement or by default). Within these restrictions, the presence of subscripts causes the size to be redefined in the statements MAT . . . ZER, MAT . . . CON, MAT . . . INPUT and MAT READ. In MAT . . . IDN the additional requirement is that the new size must be square ($n \times n$). If any size in redimensioning is non-integer, then the result is truncated to an integer size.

(e) Matrix algebra. Array sizes must conform for all these operations. Assuming arrays *A*, *B*, and *C*:

line number **MAT A = B + C**   **MAT A = A + B**   **is allowed**

line number **MAT A = B − C**   **MAT A = A − B**   **is allowed**

line number **MAT A = B∗C**   **replacement not allowed.**

(f) the **MAT READ** statement:

line number **MAT READ** *array a*, *array b* . . .

reads from the **DATA** list in row order. Redimensioning is allowed.

(g) The MAT . . . INV statement

line number **MAT** $^{array\ name}_{a}$ = **INV** $^{array\ name}_{b}$

causes *array a* to be replaced by the inverse of *array b*. The same array name cannot appear on both sides.

(h) The MAT . . . TRN statement

line number **MAT** $^{array\ name}_{a}$ = **TRN** $^{array\ name}_{b}$

causes *array a* to be replaced by the transpose of *array b*. The same array name cannot appear on both sides.

11 Supplementary Problems

PROBLEM 9.4   Solve the equations of problem 9.1 by the Gauss–Seidel iteration (without using the MAT . . . INV statement). Compare its convergence to the JACOBI iteration of problem 9.3.

PROBLEM 9.5   Rewrite the Runge–Kutta solution of problem 8.9 to make use of matrix statements.

PROBLEM 9.6   The Crank–Nicholson model of second order differentiation (problems 8.10 and 7.10) is usually thought of as being for partial differential equations. It can, however, be used as a second order method for the solution of linear ordinary differential equations (of any order). Suppose the differential equations are written as a series of first order equations (as in problem 8.9).

$$\dot{y}(t) = Ay(t) + u(t)$$

Then the Crank–Nicholson solution would be derived from estimating

$$\dot{y}(t) = \frac{y(t+h) - y(t)}{h} = \frac{Ay(t+h) - Ay(t)}{h}$$

This estimate can be used in the Taylor expansion

$$y(t+h) = y(t) + h\dot{y}(t) + \frac{h^2}{2}\ddot{y}(t) + \cdots$$

To give

$$y(t+h) = y(t) + \frac{h}{2}Ay(t) + \frac{h}{2}Ay(t+h)$$

which contains $y(t+h)$ on both sides.
However, it can be solved:

$$\left(I - \frac{hA}{2}\right)y(t+h) = \left(I + \frac{hA}{2}\right)y(t)$$

from which

$$y(t+h) = \left(I - \frac{hA}{2}\right)^{-1}\left(I + \frac{h}{2}A\right)y(t)$$
$$= Cy(t)$$

Thus for a given choice of h, the matrix C need only be found once, and the complete solution can be then worked out by successive multiplication. This method is often overlooked, which is unfortunate because it has admirable stability properties. Solve the differential equation

$$\frac{d^3y}{dt^3} + 3\frac{d^2y}{dt^3} + 2\frac{dy}{dt} = 0$$

where $y(0) = -1, \dot{y}(0) = -1, \ddot{y}(0) = -1$.

Compare the stability of this solution with that obtained using the Runge-Kutta method (problem 8.9). Which is more accurate?

PROBLEM 9.7   Matrix techniques can be used to analyse complicated electrical networks. For planar networks, one method depends on finding a set of independent equations for loop currents which are then solved by matrix inversion. In the circuit shown in Fig. 9.2, I_1, I_2, I_3 and I_4 are from independent loop currents and the voltage sources e and impedances Z are subscripted according to their positions.

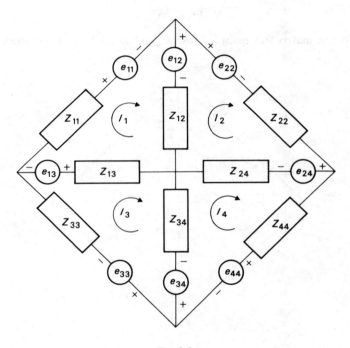

Fig. 9.2.

Considering the loop of I_1, the voltage equation around this loop is

$$Z_{11}I_1 + Z_{12}(I_1 \, I_2) + Z_{13}(I_1 - I_3) = -e_{11} - e_{12} - e_{13}$$

which can be written

$$(Z_{11} + Z_{12} + Z_{31})I_1 - Z_{12}I_2 - Z_{13}I_3 = S_1$$

where S_1 is the sum of source voltages in the loop aiding the flow of I_1. Similar equations can be derived for the other loop, leading to a matrix equation

$$ZI = S$$

where

Z = matrix of impedances whose diagonal elements are the total impedance in a loop, and off diagonal elements the negative of shared impedances.

I = vector of loop currents.

S = vector of loop source voltages.

(i) Suppose first of all that the impedances are all resistive, then the loop currents can be found as

$$I = Z^{-1}S$$

With the aid of the matrix statements of BASIC, find all the branch currents in the network of Fig. 9.3.

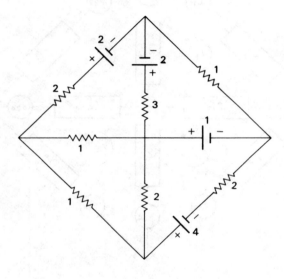

Fig. 9.3.

(ii) If some of the impedances and sources are complex, then the solution is only slightly more difficult. The matrix equation

$$ZI = S$$

could be written

$$\{ \mathscr{R}e(Z)\mathscr{R}e(i) - \mathscr{I}m(Z)\mathscr{I}m(i) \} + j\{ \mathscr{R}e(Z)\mathscr{I}m(i) + \mathscr{I}m(Z)\mathscr{R}e(i) \} = \{ \mathscr{R}e(s) + j\mathscr{I}m(s) \}$$

which leads to the double system of equations

$$\mathcal{R}e(Z).\mathcal{R}e(i) - \mathcal{I}m(Z).\mathcal{I}m(i) = \mathcal{R}e(s)$$
$$\mathcal{R}e(Z).\mathcal{I}m(i) + \mathcal{I}m(Z).\mathcal{R}e(i) = \mathcal{I}m(s)$$

which is the matrix equation.

$$\left(\begin{array}{c|c} \mathcal{R}e(z) & -\mathcal{I}m(z) \\ \hline \mathcal{I}m(z) & \mathcal{R}e(z) \end{array} \right) \left(\frac{\mathcal{R}e(i)}{\mathcal{I}m(i)} \right) = \left(\frac{\mathcal{R}e(s)}{\mathcal{I}m(s)} \right)$$

using double-sized matrices and vectors. With the aid of the matrix statements of BASIC, find all the branch currents of the unbalanced 3-phase network in Fig. 9.4.

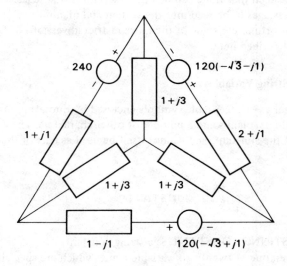

Fig. 9.4.

SESSION 10
CHARACTER STRINGS

1 Introduction

This session describes how BASIC can handle strings of alphabetic characters. Such character strings have been used as messages in PRINT statements throughout this course, in the form of string constants. It will be seen that these can be put to several further uses. The additional string variable facility allows messages to be read into the system and manipulated using several of the statements of BASIC. Unfortunately some of the more restricted versions of BASIC will allow only a few of the operations described here.

2 String Constants and String Variables

A string constant is any series of acceptable symbols enclosed by quotation marks, and can include letters, numeric digits, blanks and a number of other characters. The quotation mark itself is a delimiter, not part of the constant, and cannot itself be used as part of the string. Thus in the statement

```
77 PRINT"THIS IS A STRING CONSTANT"
```

the message 'THIS IS A STRING CONSTANT' is a string constant.

A string variable is given one of twenty six variable names which are specially reserved for this use. These names all contain two characters, the first alphabetic and the second a dollar sign $*. Thus the string variables are:

```
A$,B$,... ,Z$
```

String variables can be subscripted in one, two or three dimensions. Hence the statement

```
10 DIM A$(10)
```

defines a string array of 10 elements.

---

* It is not uncommon to find the £ sign used instead in the United Kingdom.

3 Using Character Strings in the Statements of BASIC

Meaningful operations on character strings can be performed by many of the statements of BASIC. The use of string constants in the PRINT statement will be familiar, and other uses are described below

(a) PRINT
The PRINT statement can include either string constants or string variables. The comma and semicolon used as delimiters have the usual meaning.

(b) INPUT
The INPUT statement can include string variables. When the request for input arises, quotation marks must be provided if the string being typed in includes one or more commas (because the comma is the usual delimiter for input). If there are no commas in the string, the quotation marks can be omitted. If quotation marks are included, then different strings need not be separated by commas.

EXERCISE   Experiment with the program

```
10 INPUT A$,B$
20 PRINT A$,B$
30 END
```

paying particular attention to the rules for delimiters in the INPUT statement.

Note that when asking for character input, the command 'STOP' may not work. The program

```
10 INPUT A$
20 PRINT A$
30 GO TO 10
40 END
```

could present some difficulties. If asking for input, it would be best to check for a stop message, as

```
15 IF A$="STOP"THEN 40
```

(see the IF statement, section (f) below)

(c) DATA and READ
String constants can be included in DATA statements, for example,

```
10 DATA STRING,CONSTANT
```

stores the string constants 'STRING' and 'CONSTANT' in the DATA area. As with the INPUT statement, no ambiguities can be allowed in delimiting the various constants of a DATA statement. Hence quotation marks are required if the string constant begins with a character which would confuse BASIC: blank, digit, plus sign, minus sign, or decimal point. Quotation marks must also be used if a comma appears in the string.

The READ statement can include string with variable names which should normally correspond in position with string constants in the DATA list.

(d) LET

The LET Statement may contain a string variable on the left hand side, and a string variable or constant on the right hand side. String expressions should not replace numeric variables, nor should numeric expressions replace string variables. Thus the use of LET with strings is restricted to:

$$\text{line number } \textbf{LET } \frac{\textit{string}}{\textit{variable}} = \frac{\textit{string variable}}{\textit{or constant}}$$

Note, however, that subscripted forms can be used, for example

```
575 LET A$ = X$(10)
```

(e) DIM

String variables may be explicitly defined as arrays in one, two, or three dimensions by a DIM statement. As with ordinary variables, the number of dimensions must be consistent throughout the program. If not given explicitly, the size of arrays is taken as 10 in each dimension.

(f) IF . . . THEN

A very useful application of string variables is in the IF . . . THEN statement. Two strings can be compared as

$$\text{line number } \textbf{IF } \textit{string } \frac{\textit{relational}}{\textit{operator}} \textit{ string } \textbf{THEN } \textit{line number}$$

for example

```
250 IF "ABC"<B$(I) THEN 300
```

will compare the string 'ABC' with the string element B$ (I). If 'ABC' is earlier in alphabetical order than B$ (I), then 'ABC' is considered to be less than B$, and the branch occurs to 300. 'ABC' is greater than 'ABB', equal to 'ABC', and is less than 'ABD', 'ABCA', or 'ABC '. Note the effect of the blank. Comparison between strings and arithmetic expressions is not recommended.

4 Problems

PROBLEM 10.1   Write a program which translates integer numbers into their English digits, e.g. 123 is

ONE TWO THREE

PROBLEM 10.2   Write a program which sorts a list of names into alphabetical order

PROBLEM 10.3   December 31, 1899 was a Sunday. Write a program to print the day of the week for any date after then. Leap years occur whenever the date is exactly divisible by 4, except that the exact centuries are only leap years if divisible by 400 (1900 was not, 2000 will be).

5 Summary Notes on Session 10

    (a) String constants are sequences of characters usually enclosed in quotation marks. They may be used in the statements PRINT, DATA, IF . . . THEN, and on the right hand side of the LET statement.

    (b) String variables have the names A$, B$, . . . , Z$.
They may be used in the statements INPUT, READ, IF . . . THEN, PRINT, LET, and DIM (and so may be subscripted), but not in any of the MAT statements.

    (c) In comparing strings using the IF . . . THEN statement, strings nearer the beginning of the alphabet are less than those nearer the end.

SESSION 11
SOME EXTENSIONS TO BASIC

1 Introduction

Since first appearing at Dartmouth College in 1964, BASIC has undergone a number of extensions which have not been uniformly implemented in all computer systems. The character string handling described in Session 10 is an example of an early extension which has been fairly widely adopted. In this Session, some other extensions are described which are not yet as generally available. These extensions alleviate some of the disadvantages of elementary BASIC which were pointed out in earlier Sessions. In some ways however it is best that BASIC should have obvious limitations so that the beginner eventually will turn to one of the more comprehensive languages. As BASIC is extended some of the fundamental limitations remain although they may not be obvious.

With the PRINT statement of BASIC, which was discussed in some detail in Session 5, the programmer has only limited control over the layout of his printed output. The PRINT USING statement described here allows an explicit picture of the output line to be specified by the programmer and so the exact format can be controlled.

In presenting functions and subroutines in Session 6, only the most restricted form of definition was allowed. Some versions of BASIC support multiple 'dummy arguments', multiple line functions, and subprograms whose variables are completely separate from those of the main program or any other subprogram. These additional facilities are described here.

2 Explicit Control of Output Format—the PRINT USING statement

The PRINT USING statement allows the arrangement of the output line to be controlled by the programmer. Every PRINT USING statement refers to an 'image statement' which specifies a symbolic picture of the desired printed line. The PRINT USING statement has the form

line number a **PRINT USING** *line number b*, *quantity*, *quantity* . . .

The *quantities* printed can be expressions (including as always single variables or constants), string variables, or character strings in quotation marks. The PRINT USING statement must have an associated image statement at *line number b*, of the form

line number b: *specification*

The colon identified *line number b* as an image statement. *Specification* is an explicit description of the output line showing the 'fields' or positions of printed output using groups of the symbol #, separated by blanks or other controls as outlined in the following sections.

(a) Integer numbers

The 'fields' of printing for integers are shown by groups of the symbol # in the image statement. The printed signs of these integers can also be controlled. The exercise which follows illustrates the facilities available.

EXERCISE   Try the statement

```
10 PRINT USING 20,100,-100
```

with the images

(i)   `20:#### #####`

(ii) `20:-#### -####`

(iii) `20:+#### +####`

The above exercise should clarify the following rules for signs:

(i) If no sign is given in the image, then the sign of a positive number is not printed whereas that of a negative number is printed in the leftmost position of its field.
Thus image (i) in the preceding exercise should produce the result

```
100 -  100
```

(ii) If a minus sign begins the integer field, then the signs of positive numbers are still not printed, and those of negative numbers are placed next to the most significant digit. Thus image (ii) in the preceding exercise should give the printed line

```
100   -100
```

(iii) If a plus sign begins the field then the signs of all numbers are printed next to the most significant digit as in image (iii):

```
+100   -100
```

The requirements of an image will be impossible to meet if the number is too large. In this case an * will be printed before the offending number which is then printed, with the image expanded as necessary.

EXERCISE   Try the following example of an impossible image:

```
10 PRINT USING 20,.1E05
20:##
30 END
```

It is the image, not the PRINT USING statement that makes a printed number appear as an integer. If the number is not an integer, it is truncated to an integer before printing.

EXERCISE   Verify that nonintegers are truncated to fit an integer image. For negative numbers, how does this truncation relate to the INT function?

(b) Fixed point numbers

The image for a number can fix the position of the decimal point, and the printing normally includes exactly the requested number of decimal places. The rules for signs are the same as they were for integers in (a) above. The decimal point can occupy any position in the field, including the beginning or end.

EXERCISE
(i) Try the program

```
10 PRINT USING 20,4*ATN(1),-EXP(1)
20:###.#### ###.####
30 END
```

(ii) Verify that the printing of signs is controlled exactly as for integers.
(iii) Find out what happens to fixed point numbers which are too large.
(iv) Find out what happens to negative fixed point numbers if no sign is specified and there is not room for one, e.g.

```
10 PRINT USING 20,-100
20:###.##
30 END
```

(c) Floating point numbers (exponential format)

Exponential format is specified by the placing of *exactly five* exponentiation signs ($\uparrow$) at the end of a numeric field, which must already contain a decimal point. Again the rules for signs are the same. In this case the numbers are never too large, but the number of decimal places for negative numbers will be reduced by the computer to accommodate a sign if no sign position was specified.

EXERCISE
(i) Try the program

```
10 PRINT USING 20,EXP(15),-EXP(10)
20:###.###↑↑↑↑↑ ###.###↑↑↑↑↑
30:END
```

(ii) Verify the rules for signs

(d) Character strings

Messages can be included either in the PRINT USING statement or in the image statement. It is sometimes convenient to put messages in the PRINT USING statement so that the same image can be used with different messages. When the character string is part of the PRINT USING statement, then the message is printed where the symbol # appears in the image. The image statement may be disobeyed if there is insufficient room provided for the message.

EXERCISE
(i) Try

```
10 PRINT USING 20,"MESSAGE"
20:######
30 PRINT USING 20,"SAUSAGE"
40 END
```

(ii) Find out what happens if the message is longer or shorter than the image field
(iii) Find out what happens if the image field is in error, containing for example a decimal point or a sign. In some systems the + sign produces 'concatenation' of two messages, i.e. they are joined together as in

```
10 PRINT USING 20,"WATER","GATE"
20:#####+####
```

which should print

WATERGATE

Messages can be included directly in the image statement, for example

```
10 PRINT USING 20,4*ATN(1)
20:THE VALUE OF PI TO 6 PLACES IS #.######
```

However if the message contains a symbol which would confuse BASIC such as . + − or ↑, then quotation marks must be used, for example

```
10 INPUT A,B,C,D
20 PRINT USING 30,(A+B-C)↑D
30:"(A+B-C)↑D = "-####.##↑↑↑↑↑
40 END
```

(e) *Miscellaneous comments on PRINT USING*

(i) Several PRINT USING statements can refer to the same image.
(ii) If the PRINT USING asks for more variables to be printed than there are fields in the image, then the same image is started again on the same print line, for example

```
10 PRINT USING 20,"WATER","GATE"
20:#####
30 END
```

should produce the result

WATERGATE

However successive PRINT USING statements always start new printer lines, as in

```
10 PRINT USING 30,1,2,3
20 PRINT USING 30,4,5,6
30:#   #   #
40 END
```

(iii) The PRINT USING statement is of little use in printing graphs or generating variable layouts, as there is no TAB facility in it.

3 Problems

PROBLEM 11.1   Find out how many digits of accuracy you computer can provide for π using the ATN function and for e using the EXP function.

$$\pi = 3.14159 \quad 26535 \quad 89793 \quad 23846$$
$$e = 2.71828 \quad 18284 \quad 59045 \quad 23536$$

PROBLEM 11.2   Calculate and print an interest table for investments showing the return on investments at 1%, 2%, . . . , 12% over from 1 to 25 investment periods.

$$r = (1 + i)^n$$

where r = return
i = interest rate (1% = 0.01)
n = number of periods

4 Extended Function Capabilities—multiple function parameters

The single line functions described in Session 6 were limited to a single argument, which was treated as a 'dummy argument' when the program was executed. Some versions of BASIC may allow several arguments, separated by commas.

EXERCISE   The following example should produce a result which has the magnitude of argument A and the sign of argument B. Find out if multiple arguments are allowed by trying it.

line number **DEF FNA (A, B) = SGN(B)∗ABS(A)**

If these multiple arguments are allowed, then try problems 11.3 and 11.4.

PROBLEM 11.3   (a) Provide a function which, given two arguments, finds the quotient after integer division of the first argument by the second.

(b) Provide a function which, given two arguments, finds the remainder after integer division of the first argument by the second.

PROBLEM 11.4   The ATN function can only give the arctangent in two quadrants, $-\pi/2$ to $+\pi/2$. Provide a function which given both X and Y coordinates of a point, finds the angle θ in any quadrant, as in Fig. 11.1.

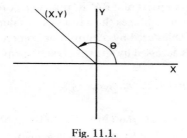

Fig. 11.1.

5 Extended Function Capabilities—multiple line functions and the FNEND statement

The usefulness of functions is obviously limited if they must be defined in a single line, as in Session 6. If a multiple line definition is available, then any of the statements of BASIC can form part of the function. To use a multiple line function the DEF FN*a* statement is used without being equated to an expression, and the FNEND statement indicates the end of the function. Somewhere within the function a value must be assigned to FN*a* in a LET statement.

Example   The following function evaluates the factorial of a number. It returns the factorial of the absolute value for a negative number, and 1 for the factorial of 0.

```
100 DEF FNF(X)
110 REM FACTORIAL OF A NUMBER
120 LET FNF = 1
130 FOR X = INT(ABS(X))TO 2 STEP -1
140 LET FNF = FNF*X
150 NEXT X
160 FNEND
```

Note that this function has avoided using any additional variables, relying only on the function name and its own argument. However, it has destroyed its own argument X, which may not always be desirable.

If multiple line functions are supported, they are likely to be allowed several arguments, and this is assumed in problem 11.6

PROBLEM 11.5   Write a function to return the largest prime factor of a given number.

PROBLEM 11.6   (a) Write a function which, given an array and its length, returns the smallest array value.

(b) Write a function which, given an array and its length, returns the subscript of the array member whose value is nearest the mean.

6 Subroutines with Local Variables—the CALL, SUB, SUBEND and SUBEXIT statements

In Session 6 a subroutine facility was described using the GOSUB and RETURN statements which should be part of all BASIC systems. In that session some care was taken to explain that variables of the same name were shared by all parts of a BASIC program. A few BASIC systems allow an additional subroutine facility which combines the advantages of dummy arguments with the convenience of having all the variables used by a subroutine completely isolated from the rest of the program. Such a subroutine is accessed by the CALL statement:

line number a **CALL** *name (parameter, parameter . . .)*

When *line number a* is reached, the program branches to the subroutine called *name.* The number and type of symbols in *name* will be restricted in some way. A safe practice would be to use only four letters or numbers in name, such as FACT or JOE1, and the first character should be a letter as in X372. The parameters are dummy arguments for the subroutine.

The subroutine *name* starts with the SUB statement

line number b **SUB** *name (variable, variable . . .)*

Thus the CALL at *line number a* causes a jump to the line following *line number b* and the parameters given in the CALL statement can be referred to using the corresponding variable names in the SUB statement. There are some restrictions on these parameters which will be listed later.

A subroutine must have a SUBEND statement as its last line:

line number **SUBEND**

and the SUBEXIT statement is also available:

line number **SUBEXIT**

Both SUBEND and SUBEXIT have the same effect in this kind of subroutine as the RETURN statement has in the more usual subroutine, with the additional purpose of SUBEND to indicate the last line of the subroutine. In this, illustrations SUBEND and SUBEXIT would each cause a jump back to the line following *line number a*. SUBEXIT would be used if a return were desired before the SUBEND had been reached, as in the example which follows.

Example   The following subroutine returns the factorial of I in variable J but prints an error message if I is negative or not an integer.

```
500 SUB FACT(I,J)
510 REM SUBROUTINE TO FIND FACTORIAL I, ANSWER RETURNED IN J
520 LET J = 1
530 REM CHECK THAT I IS POSITIVE
```

```
540 IF INT(ABS(I))=I THEN 580
550 PRINT"ILLEGAL CALL TO FACTORIAL "I"ANSWER RETURNED AS 1"
560 SUBEXIT
570 REM EVALUATE THE FACTORIAL
580 FOR K = I TO 2 STEP -1
590 LET J = J*K
600 NEXT J
610 SUBEND
```

The important advantage of this new kind of subroutine is that the variable names used in the SUB statement are 'dummies' for those used in the CALL, and every other variable name used is local to the subroutine. Therefore the variable K in the above example is a 'local' name, and its use does not affect a variable K used in another part of the program. Any DATA statements present in the subroutine are also local, and a READ in the subroutine will refer only to local DATA statements.

Example   The following subroutine will evaluate $_nC_r$ using subroutine FACT:

```
400 SUB NCR(N,R,C)
410 REM SUBROUTINE TO FIND COMBINATIONS (N,R)
420 REM ANSWER RETURNED IN C
430 CALL FACT(N,C)
440 CALL FACT(R,P)
450 LET Z = N-R
460 CALL FACT(Z,Q)
470 LET C = C*P/Q
480 SUBEND
```

In the CALL statement the parameters are restricted to the following:

(i) Scalar variable names, as in the above examples,

(ii) Array variable names in which case the number of subscripts must be given in the following way:
A( ) for an array A of one dimension
C(,) for an array C of two dimensions
D(,,) for an array D of three dimensions

Example 6 0 `CALL THIN(D(,,))`

(iii) The name of a defined function or a standard function which the subroutine can later use.

7 Problems

The following earlier problems are suitable for subroutine use:

4.11
7.4, 7.6, 7.7, 7.8, 7.9
8.5, 8.6, 8.7, 8.9
9.1, 9.4, 9.6
10.2, 10.3

8 Summary Notes on Session 11

Many BASIC systems do not support these facilities.

(a) The PRINT USING statement has the form

line number a **PRINT USING** *line number b, quantity, quantity*

An image statement must be given at *line number b*. *Quantity* can be any expression (including single variables or constants) a string variable, or a character string in quotation marks.

(b) The image statement has the form

line number b: specification

Specification is a symbolic picture of the fields in the desired printed line containing

(i) groups of the symbol # wherever information from the PRINT USING statement is to be printed.

(ii) character strings, which must be in quotation marks if any of the symbols . + — # ↑ appear

Several PRINT USING statements can refer to the same image.

(c) String output from the PRINT USING statement is printed where a corresponding group of the symbol # occurs in the image. The image is expanded if a string is longer than the corresponding field.

(d) Numbers from the PRINT USING statement are printed where a corresponding group of the symbol # occurs in the image. The style of printing of numbers is influenced by the symbols . + — ↑.

(e) The manner of printing of the sign of any number is specified by the symbols + and — which can precede a field in the following ways:

(i) No such symbol, e.g. # # # #
No sign is printed for positive numbers.
The sign of a negative number is left justified in the field, e.g. — 1
(ii) The symbol —, e.g. — # # #
No sign is printed for positive numbers, the sign of a negative number is printed adjacent to the most significant digit, e.g. —1.
(iii) The symbol +, e.g. + # # #
The sign of any number is printed adjacent to the most significant digit, e.g. +1, —1.

(f) Numbers are truncated to integers if only a group of the symbol # is given. If the number is too large for the field, the symbol * is printed before the number and the image is expanded.

(g) Numbers are printed in fixed point format if only the symbol . is added to a field, e.g. # #. # #. If the number is negative and no sign is specified, one decimal place could be removed to make the number fit. Otherwise, if the number is too large for the field, the symbol * is printed before the number and the image is expanded.

(h) Numbers are printed in floating point (exponential) format if exactly five of the symbol ↑ are added to the end of the field and the decimal place is given, e.g. ##.##↑↑↑↑↑. Such a number will never be too large for the field, but the number of decimal places will be reduced by one if a sign is not specified and the number is negative.

(i) If the PRINT USING statement has more quantities than the image has fields, then the image is started again from the beginning on the same line of printed output. If there is too much output for a line, then it is continued on a new line.

(j) Some BASIC systems allow functions of several variables in the DEF FN statement:

line number **DEF FN***a* (*variable, variable . . .*) = *expression*

(k) Some BASIC systems allow a multiple line definition of functions which begin with a DEF FN statement:

line number **DEF FN***a* (*variable, variable, . . .*)

The multiple line definition must include an assignment of the function value:

line number **LET FN***a* = *expression*

and later be terminated by the FNEND statement:

line number **FNEND**

(l) Some BASIC systems support a subroutine facility with isolated local variables and dummy arguments. Such a subroutine is reached by the CALL statement:

line number **CALL** *name* (*parameter, parameter, . . .*)

subroutine *name* has the SUB statement as its first line:

line number **SUB** *name* (*variable, variable, . . .*)

Name can be a mixture of alphabetic and numeric symbols, starting with an alphabetic character. There will be a limit to the number of symbols in *name*.

The *variables* in the SUB statement are dummies for the *parameters* used in the CALL statement. Any reference to these variables in the subroutine is in fact a reference to the *parameters* in the CALL. All other variable names in the subroutine are local to the sub-routine, as are all DATA and READ statements. The *parameters* of the CALL statement are restricted to the following:

(i) Scalar variable names.

(ii) Array variable names, in which case the number of subscripts must be specified in the following way:

A( ) for an array A of one dimension

A(,) for an array C of two dimensions

A(,,) for an array D of three dimensions

(iii) The name of a defined function or a standard function which the subroutine can later use.

The subroutine returns to the calling program by means of either the SUBEXIT or SUBEND statements:

line number **SUBEXIT**

line number **SUBEND**

The last statement of the subroutine must be a SUBEND statement.

APPENDIX
A SUMMARY OF THE BASIC LANGUAGE

Where indicated, this summary may describe facilities not available on some BASIC systems. Otherwise it is intended to describe as far as possible a universal subset of BASIC. Some systems will support facilities not described here, including additional commands, additional functions, and file manipulation statements.

1 BASIC Programs

A program in BASIC consists of numbered statements, or lines, of the form

line number statement

Example

```
10 PRINT 5/7
20 END
```

When a BASIC program is executed, using the command RUN, the statements are obeyed in order of their line numbers unless the program itself dictates otherwise. The last line of every BASIC program must be an END Statement.

2 Commands

Every BASIC system should support at least the following three commands, or some equivalent:

(i) RUN—the current BASIC program is executed
(ii) LIST—the current BASIC program is printed on the terminal
(iii) NEW—the current BASIC program is 'scratched' or lost so that a new one may be commenced. On at least one system this command is SCRATCH.

3 Creating BASIC Programs

All keyboard entries to the BASIC system, except when a program is running, will be interpreted as statements if the line begins with a number. Otherwise they will be interpreted as commands.

(a) Entering—programs are entered by typing each line with a line number and ending with the 'carriage return' key. (Session 1)
(b) Correcting—a line is replaced by typing the replacement in full, including the line number and the 'carriage return' key. (Session 1)

(c) Correcting lines while typing—the symbol ← ('back arrow') or __ ('underline') eliminates the character before it. (Session 1)

(d) Inserting—a new line is inserted between two others by the use of a suitable line number. (Session 1)

(e) Deleting—a line is deleted by typing only the line number and 'carriage return' (Session 1)

4 Numbers in BASIC

Numbers in BASIC can be expressed in three forms:

(a) Integers—a number written without a decimal point, e.g. 123

(b) A number written with a decimal point, e.g. 3.1416

(c) Exponential—a number written with an exponent indicated by the letter E, e.g. 1E10 means 1×10^{10}. (Session 1)

5 Variables in BASIC—scalars, arrays, subscripts and strings

(a) Ordinary variables which represent numeric values in BASIC can be assigned any of 286 names which are the single letters:

$$A, B, C, \ldots Z$$

or any letter plus a single digit:

$$A\emptyset, A1, \ldots A9$$
$$B\emptyset, B1, \ldots B9$$
$$Z\emptyset, Z1, \ldots Z9 \qquad \text{(Session 1)}$$

(b) Some BASIC systems allow string variables which are identified by the 26 names:

$$A\$, B\$, \ldots Z\$ \qquad \text{(Session 10)}$$

(c) Scalars

A variable is scalar if it is written without a subscript in which case it represents a single value, e.g. X7.

(d) Arrays

A variable is an array if it is written with up to three subscripts, in which case it represents a list of values, e.g. Q$ (9), N(I, J), T(1, 2, 3). An array must always have the same number of subscripts. (Sessions 7, 8, 9)

(e) Subscripts

A subscript can be any arithmetic expression, however the resulting value must be between 1 and the maximum array size (some systems allow it to be $\emptyset$). Noninteger subscripts are truncated to integers (Session 7)

(f) Array sizes

The maximum size of an array is set up by the DIM statement, or by default to 10 in each subscript if no DIM statement is given. Certain matrix statements of BASIC alter the working size of an array within the constraint of the maximum array size. (Session 10)

6 Character String Constants

(a) String constants are sequences of symbols usually enclosed in quotation marks, e.g. 'HELLO SAILOR'. They may be used in the PRINT statement (Session 1). Some systems may allow their use in DATA, IF . . . THEN, and on the right hand side of the LET statement (Session 10).

(b) String variables are supported by some systems in which case the 26 variable names used are A$, B$, . . . Z$. They may be used in the statements INPUT, PRINT, READ, IF . . . THEN, LET and DIM (and so may be subscripted) but not in the MAT statements (Session 10).

(c) In comparing strings using the IF . . . THEN statement, strings nearer the beginning of the alphabet are less than those nearer the end. (Session 10).

e.g. "AB" is less than "AC"
"AB" is less than "ABA"

7 Arithmetic Expressions

BASIC arithmetic uses the hierarchy of operations

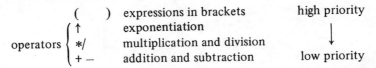

Operations of equal priority are performed from left to right. Arithmetic expressions may be written involving these operations and any variables or constants, e.g. (A+3)/D(I).

A single variable or constant is itself a valid expression.

Two operators may not appear together, e.g. A+−B is not allowed. Operators normally separate two values, e.g. 3∗B, but the operator−has 'unary' meaning, e.g. −J or 3∗(−B). (Session 1)

8 Relational Expressions

(a) Relational expressions are written

arithmetic	*relational*	*arithmetic*
expression	*operator*	*expression*

e.g. A > B

The result of a relational expression is TRUE or FALSE.

Relational expressions are used in the IF . . . THEN statement. (Session 2)

(b) The available relational operators are

$$
\begin{array}{ll}
= & \text{equal to} \\
> & \text{greater than} \\
< & \text{less than} \\
>= \text{ or } => & \text{greater or equal} \\
<= \text{ or } =< & \text{less or equal} \\
<> \text{ or } >< & \text{not equal}
\end{array}
$$

(Session 2)

(c) In some systems relational expressions can be more complicated involving the additional operations AND and OR (inclusive) as in

```
(A>B*1Ø)OR(C<=1)
```

(d) In some systems the results TRUE or FALSE have the values 1 and 0 and can be used as part of any arithmetic expression.

(e) In some systems the string relational expression is available;

$$string \; {relational \atop operator} \; string$$

e.g. ``"ABC">=B$(I)``

(Session 10)

9 Library Functions

All BASIC systems should support the following set of library functions:

Function	Meaning
SIN (x)	The sine of x where x is an angle in radians
COS (x)	The cosine of x where x is in radians
TAN (x)	The tangent of x where x is in radians
ATN (x)	The arctangent of an angle x in the range $-\pi/2$ to $+\pi/2$ radians
EXP (x)	The value of e^x
LOG (x)	The natural logarithm of x
ABS (x)	The absolute value of x
SQR (x)	The square root of x
INT (x)	The largest integer not greater than x. Example: INT $(5.95) = 5$ and INT $(-5.95) = -6$
SGN (x)	The sign of x, has value 1 if x is positive; 0 if x is 0; or -1 if x is negative

In the above functions, x represents any expression, which may of course include other functions. The quantity x is called the argument or parameter of the function. (Session 1)

A function RND, which is a random number generator, appears in most versions of BASIC. It does not always have an argument — if it does, the argument may not have a meaning.

The TAB function is a special function associated with the PRINT statement, as described in section 11 of this appendix.

10 Statements—General

The statements of BASIC are summarized here in alphabetical order. The details of the statements used for functions and subroutines and for matrix operations are listed separately, in sections 11 and 12. Items in square brackets are optional.

line number **CALL** *name* [*(parameter, parameter . . .)*]
  This statement is used for subroutine linkage. See section 12 of this appendix.

  (Session 11)

line number **DATA** *constant, constant . . .*
  The *constants* given in the DATA statement are stored in the computer in the order given. Successive DATA statements add to the list in order. Information from the list is assigned to variables by the READ or MAT READ statements. (Session 8)
  Some systems allow strings to be defined in the DATA statement, and the quotation marks can be left out if the string does not contain blanks, plus signs, digits, minus signs, decimal points, or commas.

  E.g. `15 DATA STRING,"STRING+31"`

  (Session 10)

  In a system which supports the SUB statement, DATA statements in a subroutine are local to that subroutine.

  (Session 11)

line number **DEF FN**a *(variable)* = *expression*
  This statement is used for function definition and may take other forms. See section 12 of this appendix.

  (Session 6)

line number **DIM** *subscripted variable, subscripted variable . . .*
  The DIM statement specifies the maximum size of arrays. In the DIM statement the subscripts must be integer numbers. The size specified is the working size of the arrays, but some of the MAT statements can change the working size within the limits of the maximum. If an array is not mentioned in a DIM statement, the maximum is 10 in each subscript.

  (Session 8)

line number **END**
  The END statement must be the last in any BASIC programs, i.e. it must be present and have the highest line number. When it is encountered the execution of a BASIC program terminates.

  (Session 1)

  To terminate a program before the highest line number, the STOP statement is used.

  (Session 6)

line number **FNEND**
  This statement is used in the definition of functions in some systems. See section 12 of this appendix.

  (Session 11)

line number **FOR** *variable* = *expression a* **TO** *expression b* [**STEP** *expression c*]

The FOR statement begins a FOR . . . NEXT program loop, which is repeated with the named variable having the initial value given by *expression a* and changing by *expression b* until *expression c* is reached. The word STEP and *expression c* are optional, and if not given the requirement is taken as 1. The named *variable* can be adjusted during the loop, but the initial, final, and step values are fixed when the loop first begins and cannot later be changed. With care, a program can jump out of and into loops. The end of a loop is indicated by a NEXT statement, which must be present. FOR . . . NEXT loops using different *variables* may be nested.

(Session 6)

line number a **GOSUB** *line number b*

This statement is used to call a subroutine. See section 12 of this appendix.

(Session 6)

line number a **GO TO** *line number b*

The GO TO statement causes a jump to *line number b*.

(Session 1)

line number a **IF** *relational expression* **THEN** *line number b*

When the IF statement is encountered, the *relational expression* is evaluated and if it is TRUE, then the program jumps to *line number b*. If the *relational expression* is FALSE, the execution continues from the next line after *line number a*.

(Session 2)

line number **INPUT** *variable, variable* . . .

The INPUT statement causes the computer to request information by typing the symbol ?, and waiting until a line of information is entered.

Exactly the correct number of quantities should be entered, separated by commas. If too few are entered an explanatory message is given and the missing information should be typed in. If too many are entered a different explanatory message appears and it will be necessary to type all the information again from the beginning.

(Session 1)

line number **LET** *variable* = *expression*

In the LET statement the expression on the right hand side is evaluated and the result replaces the value of the variable on the left hand side.

(Session 2)

line number **MAT** *variable* = *variable* + *variable*
line number **MAT** *variable* = *variable* − *variable*
line number **MAT** *variable* = *variable* ∗ *variable*
line number **MAT** *variable* = (*expression*) ∗ *variable*
line number **MAT** *variable* = **CON** [(*subscripts*)]
line number **MAT** *variable* = **IDN** [(*subscripts*)]
line number **MAT** *variable* = **INV** (*variable*)
line number **MAT** *variable* = **TRN** (*variable*)
line number **MAT** *variable* = **ZER** [(*subscripts*)]
line number **MAT INPUT** *variable, variable,* . . .
line number **MAT PRINT** *variable delimiter variable* . . .
line number **MAT READ** *variable, variable,* . . .

These statements are the special matrix facilities of BASIC. See section 13 of this appendix.

(Session 9)

line number **NEXT** *variable*

The NEXT statement identifies the end of the FOR . . . NEXT loop in which the variable was the one used in the FOR statement

(Session 4)

line number a **ON** *expression* **GO TO** *line number b*, *line number c*, . . .
    The ON . . . GO TO statement allows a multiple choice of branches to the destinations given in *line number b*, *line number c*, ... The *expression* is evaluated and truncated to an integer. If the result is 1, the program jumps to *line number b*, if 2 to *line number c*, etc. If the *expression* is negative, zero, or too large for the number of destinations given, an error message is produced. (Session 4)

line number **PRINT** *quantity delimiter quantity* . . .
line number a **PRINT USING** *line number b*, *quantity*, *quantity*, . . .
line number b: *specification*

    These statements produce printed output. See section 11 of this appendix.

line number **READ** *variable*, *variable* . . .
    The READ statement assigns values to the named *variables* from the list defined by DATA statements. As successive READ statements are encountered, they continue through the DATA list. In some systems the *variables* may be string variables. In systems with the SUB statement, READ statements in a subroutine read from a local DATA list. (Session 8)

line number **REM** *any remark or comment*
    The REM statement has no effect on the execution of a BASIC program, and is provided to allow remarks to be inserted to explain the program. (Session 2)

line number **RESTORE**
    The RESTORE statement returns subsequent READ statements to the beginning of the DATA list. (Session 8)

line number **RETURN**
    This statement is used in subroutines. See section 12 of this appendix. (Session 6)

line number **STOP**
    This statement terminates the execution of a program and is used when a program is to stop before the last line (which is the END statement) (Session 6)

line number **SUB** *name* (*argument*, *argument*)
line number **SUBEND**
line number **SUBEXIT**
    These statements are part of the subroutine facilities on some systems. See section 12 of this appendix. (Session 11)

11 Statements–Printed Output

All BASIC systems support the PRINT statement:

line number **PRINT** *quantity delimiter quantity delimiter* . . .

    where *quantity* can be

(a) an expression resulting in numerical output
(b) a character string in quotation marks resulting in literal output

(c) on some systems, a string variable resulting in literal output
(d) the TAB function

and *delimiter* can be a comma or semicolon, and can sometimes be omitted as explained below.

A PRINT statement starts a new line unless a final *delimiter* was explicitly given in the previous PRINT, in which case it continues on the same line.
A PRINT statement containing too many *quantities* for a single printed line will be continued on the following line.

The comma:

The print line is divided into 5 zones of 15 spaces.
The comma causes the next *quantity* to be printed beginning in the first space of the next zone.

The semicolon:

between *quantities* causes the output to be compressed. After a TAB function or a character string printing continues in the next space. Between numerical output the spacing depends on the numbers (see (d)), for example the field width for small integers is 6 spaces. At the end of a print statement the semicolon causes the next print statement to continue on the same line.

Numbers:

may appear in the printed output as integers, or as numbers with decimal places, or in exponential format.

Character strings:

The quotation marks surrounding character strings enable the *delimiter* to be left out, in which case a semicolon is assumed, except at the end of a PRINT statement where the absence of a *delimiter* causes the next PRINT statement to start a new line.

The TAB function:

TAB (*expression*) may appear as a *quantity* in a PRINT statement. This causes the printer to move forward to the column number given by the integer part of the *expression*. The *expression* must specify a column number which exists, and the printer cannot move backwards.

The PRINT USING statement is available only on some BASIC systems:

line number a **PRINT USING** *line number b, quantity, quantity* . . .
An image statement must be given at *line number b. Quantity* can be any expression (including single variables or constants), a string variable, or a character string in quotation marks.

The image statement has the form
line number b: specification
   Specification is a symbolic picture of the fields in the desired printed line containing:

(a) groups of the symbol # wherever information from the PRINT USING statement is to be printed.
(b) Character strings, which must be in quotation marks if any of the symbols . + – # ↑ appear

Several PRINT USING statements can refer to the same image.

String output from the PRINT USING statement is printed where a corresponding group of the symbol # occurs in the image. The image is expanded if a string is longer than the corresponding field.

Numbers from the PRINT USING statement are printed where a corresponding group of the symbol # occurs in the image. The style of printing of numbers is influenced by the symbols . + – ↑.

The manner of printing of the sign of any number is specified by the symbols + and – which can precede a field in the following cases:

(a) no such symbol, e.g. # # # #
No sign is printed for positive numbers; the sign of a negative number is left justified in the field, e.g.   –   1
(b) the symbol –, e.g. – # # #
No sign is printed for positive numbers; the sign of a negative number is printed adjacent to the most significant digit, e.g.   – 1
(c) the symbol +, e.g. + # # #
The sign of any number is printed adjacent to the most significant digit, e.g.   + 1   – 1

Numbers are truncated to integers if only a group of the symbol # is given. If the number is too large for the field, the symbol * is printed before the number and the image is expanded.

Numbers are printed in fixed point format if only the symbol • is added to a field e.g. # # . # # . If the number is negative and no sign is specified, one decimal place could be removed to make the number fit. Otherwise, if the number is too large for the field, the symbol * is printed before the number and the image is expanded.

Numbers are printed in floating point (exponential) format if exactly five of the symbol ↑ are added to the end of the field and the decimal place is given, e.g. # # . # # ↑ ↑ ↑ ↑ ↑ . Such a number will never be too large for the field, but the number of decimal places will be reduced by one if a sign is not specified and the number is negative.

If the PRINT USING statement has more *quantities* than the image has fields, then the image is started again from the beginning on the same line of printed output. If there is too much output for a line, then it is continued on a new line.   (Session 11)

12 Statements–Functions and Subroutines

(a) Functions

All BASIC systems support the single line function:

line number **DEF FN**a *(variable) = expression*
> *a* can be the letters A through Z, thus the 26 names, FNA, FNB, . . . FNZ are available.

When the function name is implicitly used in a running program, the *expression* on the right hand side is evaluated using the given value of the function *variable*. The function *variable* is thus a 'dummy' for the value used while running.
Only one definition of a particular function should be used.
Functions may use other functions, but endless loops may not be so established.

Some BASIC systems allow functions of several variables in the DEF FN statement:
line number **DEF FN**a *(variable, variable, . . .) = expression*

Some BASIC systems allow a multiple line definition of functions which begin with a DEF FN statement:
line number **DEF FN**a *[(variable, variable, . . .)]*
> The program must contain an assignment of the function value, such as

line number **LET FN**a *= expression*
> and later be terminated by the FNEND statement:

line number **FNEND**

(b) Subroutines

Subroutines are called by the GOSUB statement:

line number a **GOSUB** *line number b*
> The running program continues from *line number b* until a RETURN is encountered, when it carries on from the line after *line number a*. Subroutines may call other subroutines, but endless loops may not be so established.

Subroutines are ended by the RETURN statement:
line number **RETURN**
> The running program returns to the line after the latest GOSUB.

The STOP statement terminates program execution:
line number **STOP**

Some BASIC systems support a subroutine facility with isolated local variables and dummy arguments. Such a subroutine is reached by the CALL statement:
line number **CALL** *name [(parameter, parameter . . .])*

Subroutine *name* has the SUB statement as its first line:
line number **SUB** *name [(variable, variable . . .)]*

> *Name* can be a mixture of alphabetic and numeric symbols, starting with an alphabetic character. There will be a limit to the number of symbols in *name*.

The *variables* in the SUB statement are dummies for the *parameters* used in the CALL statement. Any reference to these *variables* in the subroutine is in fact a reference to the *parameters* in the CALL. All other variable names in the subroutine are local to the subroutine, as are all DATA and READ statements.

The *parameters* of the CALL statement are restricted to the following:

(i) Scalar variable names

(ii) Array variable names, in which case the number of subscripts must be specified in the following way

A( ) for an array A of one dimension

C(,) for an array C of two dimensions

D(,,) for an array D of three dimensions

(iii) The name of a defined function or a standard function which the subroutine can later use.

The subroutine returns to the calling program by means of either the SUBEXIT or SUBEND statements:

line number **SUBEXIT**

line number **SUBEND**

The last statement of the subroutine must be a SUBEND statement.

13 Statements–Matrix Facilities

Nearly all BASIC systems will support the special matrix statements, all beginning with the keyword MAT, and these provide a variety of useful array manipulations. Any array variable of one or two dimensions can use the matrix facilities, but the number of subscripts used must always be consistent. The algebraic facilities require conformability of the matrices used. Some of the other facilities can redimension an array within its maximum size as given in the DIM statement, or by default as 10 in each subscript (see note (c)).

(a) Defining special matrices

Three statements are provided for defining a unit matrix, a matrix of all zeros and a matrix of all ones. These statements allow redimensioning (see note (c))

line number **MAT** $\frac{array}{name}$ **= ZER**

defines the *named array* to have all zeros.

line number **MAT** $\frac{array}{name}$ **= CON**

defines the *named array* to have all ones.

$$\textit{line number } \mathbf{MAT} \begin{smallmatrix} array \\ name \end{smallmatrix} = \mathbf{IDN}$$

defines the *named array* as a unit matrix. The matrix so defined must be square.

These facilities cannot be mixed or used in combination with the algebraic facilities. Thus

```
22 MAT C = CON + IDN
```

is not allowed.

(b) The MAT READ statement

line number **MAT READ** *array a , array b . . .*
Reads the named arrays one at a time in row order from the DATA list. Redimensioning is allowed (see note (c)).

(c) Matrix redimensioning

The statements in sections (a) and (b) above allow redimensioning. The number of subscripts cannot be changed, and the original total number of array elements cannot be exceeded (whether specified in a DIM statement or by default). Within these restrictions the presence of subscripts causes the size to be changed in the statements MAT . . . ZER, MAT . . . CON, MAT . . . INPUT, and MAT . . . READ. If the redimensioning subscripts are not integers they are truncated.

Example

```
20 MAT C = CON(20,10)
```

Provided C was an array of two dimensions and had been given at least 200 elements in a DIM statement, it becomes an array of all ones of size 20 x 10.

The MAT . . . IDN statement can also redimension an array with the additional restriction that the new size must be square (n x n).

(d) Matrix algebra

Four statements are available for matrix algebra, and for all these operations the sizes of the arrays must conform. These four facilities cannot be combined in a single statement.

Matrix addition

$$\textit{line number } \mathbf{MAT} \begin{smallmatrix} array \\ name \ a \end{smallmatrix} = \begin{smallmatrix} array \\ name \ b \end{smallmatrix} + \begin{smallmatrix} array \\ name \ c \end{smallmatrix}$$

The *named arrays* must all have the same dimensions. *Array b* is added to *array c* element by element and the result replaces *array a*. Self-replacement is allowed, so the following statement is legal:

```
55 MAT A = A + B
```

Matrix subtraction

line number **MAT** $\underset{name\ a}{array} = \underset{name\ b}{array} - \underset{name\ c}{array}$

The *named arrays* must all have the same dimensions. *Array c* is subtracted from *array b* element by element and the result replaces *array b*. Self-replacement is allowed, so that the following statement is legal:

```
55 MAT A = A - B
```

Multiplication of an array by a scalar

line number **MAT** $\underset{name\ a}{array} = (expression)* \underset{name\ b}{array}$

Array a must have the same dimensions as *array b*.
The *expression* is evaluated to give a scalar number, which is multiplied by each term of *array b*. The result replaces *array a*. Self-replacement is allowed, as in

```
55 MAT A = (3)*A
```

A useful application of this statement is in the simple replacement of one array by another. BASIC does not allow

```
60 MAT A = B
```

but it does allow

```
60 MAT A = (1)*B
```

Matrix multiplication

$$\text{line number } \mathbf{MAT} \ \underset{\text{name a}}{\text{array}} = \underset{\text{name b}}{\text{array}} * \underset{\text{name c}}{\text{array}}$$

The *array b* is multiplied by the *array c* and the result replaces the *array a*. *Array b* must have the same number of columns as *array c* has rows. *Array a* must have the same number of rows as *array b* and the same number of columns as *array c*. These could be scalars, vectors, or matrices in the combinations tabulated in Session 9. Self-replacement is *not* allowed, hence

$$3\emptyset \ \mathsf{MAT} \ \ \mathsf{A} \ = \ \mathsf{A*B} \quad \text{is } illegal$$

(e) Matrix inversion and transposition

$$\text{line number } \mathbf{MAT} \ \underset{\text{name a}}{\text{array}} = \mathbf{INV} \left(\underset{\text{name b}}{\text{array}} \right)$$

Array b is inverted and the result replaces *array a*. Both arrays must be square and of the same size. Self-replacement is not allowed.

$$\text{line number } \mathbf{MAT} \ \underset{\text{name a}}{\text{array}} = \mathbf{TRN} \left(\underset{\text{name b}}{\text{array}} \right)$$

The transpose of *array b* replaces *array a*. Both arrays must be square. Self-replacement is not allowed.

INDEX